There's plenty of action and thrills in this match at Selhurst Park, home of Crystal Palace, and there's lots more to come on the following pages of this super SCORCHER Annual.

95p

THE STORY OF THE EUROPEAN CHAMPIONS' CUP

WHAT HAD BEEN, UNTIL THEN, ONLY A DREAM, BECAME A REALITY IN SEPTEMBER, 1955, — THE EUROPEAN CUP WAS BORN. 16 CLUBS, CHAMPIONS OF THEIR RESPECTIVE COUNTRIES, FOUGHT OUT THE FIRST TOURNAMENT. THE CAPTAINS OF REIMS AND REAL MADRID EXCHANGE PENNANTS (RIGHT), BEFORE THE FIRST FINAL IN PARIS, IN JUNE, 1956 . . . .

IT WAS AN EXCITING FINAL . . . REIMS TOOK THE LEAD TWICE BEFORE RIAL, WITH HIS SECOND GOAL OF THE MATCH, GAVE REAL MADRID A 4-3 WIN, AND THE CUP. IT WAS THE START OF MADRID'S LONG REIGN . . . .

124,000 FANS SAW THE NEXT EUROPEAN CUP FINAL IN MADRID. PLAYING FIORENTINA ON THEIR HOME GROUND, REAL HAD TO WAIT UNTIL 20 MINUTES FROM THE END BEFORE ALFREDO DI STEFANO PUT THEM IN FRONT (LEFT), FROM THE PENALTY SPOT. REAL WON 2-0. SO DI STEFANO (RIGHT), BECAME THE UNCROWNED "KING" OF EUROPE.

REAL MADRID WON THE FIRST FOUR EUROPEAN CUPS, AND REACHED THE PEAK OF THEIR FORM IN MAY, 1960, WHEN THEY MET EINTRACHT FRANKFURT IN THEIR FIFTH SUCCESSIVE FINAL. IT WAS PLAYED AT HAMPDEN PARK, IN FRONT OF 135,000 DELIGHTED FANS. EINTRACHT SHOCKED THE SPANIARDS, SCORING FIRST!

. . . BUT THEN DI STEFANO (THREE GOALS), AND FERENC PUSKAS (FOUR), GOT BUSY, UNSTOPPABLE. MADRID RAN OUT 7-3 WINNERS . . . THEIR FIFTH WIN!

NOT ONLY HAD REAL MADRID HELD THE CUP FOR THE FIRST FIVE YEARS IT WAS PLAYED FOR, BUT THE GREAT DI STEFANO HAD SCORED IN *EVERY ONE* OF THOSE FINALS.

MANCHESTER UNITED HAD BEEN THE FIRST TEAM FROM ENGLAND TO TRY THEIR LUCK IN THE EUROPEAN CUP. FOOTBALL LEAGUE CHAMPIONS IN *1956*, THEY'D REACHED THE SEMI-FINAL IN *1957*, BUT MADRID HAD PROVED TOO STRONG FOR THEM. HERE (LEFT), UNITED'S FINE CENTRE-FORWARD TOMMY TAYLOR SCORES, IN MADRID, BUT REAL WON 3-1 AND HELD THAT LEAD IN THE SECOND-LEG AT OLD TRAFFORD.

IT WAS RETURNING FROM A EUROPEAN CUP MATCH IN BELGRADE, IN FEBRUARY, *1958*, WHEN MANCHESTER UNITED'S ?PLANE CRASHED AT MUNICH AIRPORT.... EIGHT PLAYERS WERE KILLED, INCLUDING TOMMY TAYLOR, AND A GREAT TEAM WAS WIPED OUT. COULD UNITED RECOVER FROM THIS CRUEL BLOW?

IN *1960-61* REAL MADRID TASTED DEFEAT IN A EUROPEAN CUP TIE FOR THE FIRST TIME. BARCELONA, ALSO FROM SPAIN, BEAT THEM *4-3* AFTER TWO THRILLING MATCHES.

BUT BARCELONA DIDN'T WIN THE CUP. ALTHOUGH THEY OUTPLAYED BENFICA IN THE FINAL, IN BERNE, AND SCORED THE FIRST GOAL (ABOVE), THEY LOST. TWO MISTAKES BY THEIR INTERNATIONAL GOALKEEPER, RAMALLETS, COST BARCELONA THE CUP. BENFICA WON *3-2*....

SPEEDY WINGER FRANCISCO GENTO (ABOVE), AND MIGHTY HUNGARIAN FERENC PUSKAS (RIGHT), WERE OTHER STARS OF THE GREAT REAL MADRID SIDE. PUSKAS GOT ANOTHER HAT-TRICK IN THE *1962* FINAL — BUT BENFICA BEAT REAL *5-3*....

EUSEBIO — THE "BLACK PANTHER" — WAS OUTSTANDING IN THE BENFICA ATTACK. HE'D SCORED TWICE IN THAT VICTORY OVER REAL IN *1962*....

REAL MADRID'S REIGN BEING OVER, BENFICA, WITH TWO SUCCESSIVE TRIUMPHS, WERE ON THE THRONE, BUT THIS GOAL (LEFT), BY ALTAFINI OF A.C. MILAN, TOPPLED THEM IN THE *1963* FINAL, AT WEMBLEY.

MANCHESTER UNITED RENEWED THEIR BID FOR EUROPE'S TOP HONOUR IN *1965-66.* GEORGE BEST WAS THE HERO OF A GREAT **5-1** VICTORY IN LISBON, OVER BENFICA, IN THE QUARTER FINALS.... BUT NO — UNITED WERE BEATEN IN THE NEXT ROUND....

SO THE HONOUR OF BEING THE FIRST BRITISH CLUB TO REACH THE EUROPEAN CUP FINAL FELL TO CELTIC, IN **1967.** THEY MET INTER-MILAN (RIGHT), IN THE FINAL, IN LISBON....

CELTIC HAD ALREADY WON EVERY HONOUR THERE WAS TO WIN IN **1967,** IN SCOTLAND, AND KNEW ONLY ONE WAY TO PLAY — **ATTACK!** NOT DISMAYED BY LOSING AN EARLY GOAL TO THE ITALIANS, THEY KEPT GOING FORWARD. THE EQUALISER, WHEN IT CAME, WAS A BEAUTY — FULL-BACK TOMMY GEMMELL HITTING THE NET (ABOVE), WITH A TREMENDOUS SHOT.....

THERE WAS ONLY ONE TEAM IN IT.... THE SCOTTISH FANS WHO HAD MADE THE LONG TRIP TO PORTUGAL ROARED ON THEIR FAVOURITES. INTER-MILAN DEFENDED DESPERATELY, BUT STEVE CHALMERS STUCK IN THE VITAL GOAL (LEFT), AND THE FINAL WHISTLE SOON FOLLOWED. CELTIC HAD WON A FAMOUS VICTORY....

IT WAS, TOO, A VICTORY FOR ATTACKING FOOTBALL. INSPIRED BY THEIR POPULAR MANAGER, JOCK STEIN, CELTIC HAVE ALWAYS BEEN A CREDIT TO THE EUROPEAN CUP WITH THEIR ATTRACTIVE STYLE.

BOBBY CHARLTON SHAKES HANDS WITH MARIO COLUNA OF BENFICA, BEFORE THE 1968 FINAL...

MANCHESTER UNITED, AT LONG LAST, HAD REACHED THE EUROPEAN CUP FINAL. IT WAS PLAYED AT WEMBLEY, AND BENFICA AGAIN PROVED TOUGH OPPONENTS. CHARLTON PLAYED A CAPTAIN'S GAME, AND HEADED UNITED'S FIRST GOAL PAST HENRIQUE...

BUT BENFICA EQUALISED, AND MIGHT HAVE SNATCHED VICTORY BUT FOR A SENSATIONAL SAVE BY 'KEEPER ALEX STEPNEY. THE SCORES WERE STILL LEVEL AT THE END OF NINETY MINUTES. UNITED HAD SEEN VICTORY SLIP AWAY, AND THEIR MANAGER MATT BUSBY HAD TO ENCOURAGE HIS TIRED PLAYERS (LEFT), TO GO ON FIGHTING IN EXTRA-TIME....

EUSEBIO (LEFT), WAS STILL BENFICA'S DANGER MAN, ALREADY HE'D CAUSED UNITED ANXIOUS MOMENTS WITH HIS HARD-SHOOTING.... COULD HE WIN THE MATCH?

IT WAS GEORGE BEST, HOWEVER, WHO TILTED THE GAME UNITED'S WAY. WITH ONE FLASH OF HIS GENIUS, HE LEFT THE BENFICA DEFENDERS IN HIS TRACKS, AND STROKED THE BALL INTO THE NET... HOW THE MANCHESTER FANS IN THE 100,000 CROWD ROARED WITH DELIGHT! NO STOPPING UNITED NOW.....

WITHIN EIGHT MINUTES, FURTHER GOALS BY BRIAN KIDD AND CHARLTON MADE VICTORY SECURE... 4-1, AND HOW FITTING THAT UNITED, THE FIRST ENGLISH CLUB TO ENTER THE EUROPEAN CUP, SHOULD BECOME THE FIRST ENGLISH CLUB TO WIN IT....

IN 1969, ANOTHER COUNTRY, HOLLAND, CAME INTO THE PICTURE ... BUT AJAX OF AMSTERDAM WERE BEATEN 4-1 BY A.C. MILAN, PIERINO PRATI SCORING A HAT-TRICK — A RARE FEAT IN A EUROPEAN CUP FINAL....

THE OTHER GREAT DUTCH CLUB SIDE, FEYENOORD, GOT TO THE FINAL A YEAR LATER, AFTER KNOCKING OUT A.C. MILAN IN AN EARLIER ROUND. THERE THEY MET CELTIC (RIGHT), WHO HAD LICKED THE ENGLISH CHAMPS, LEEDS, IN THE SEMI-FINAL ...

AJAX WON THE CUP IN 1971, 1972 AND 1973. HERE JOHAN CRUYFF HEADS THEIR SECOND GOAL IN THE 1972 FINAL AGAINST INTER-MILAN, IN ROTTERDAM.

BUT IF CELTIC WERE FAVOURITES, THEY WERE IN FOR A SHOCK! ISRAEL PUT FEYENOORD AHEAD (ABOVE). GEMMELL WAS AGAIN CELTIC'S SCORER, BUT THEIR OPPONENTS GOT A DESERVED WINNING GOAL IN EXTRA-TIME.

CRUYFF (LEFT), BECAME THE NEW "KING" OF EUROPEAN SOCCER, PLAYING BRILLIANTLY IN ALL THREE OF AJAX'S SUCCESSFUL FINALS, BEFORE HIS BIG TRANSFER.

IN 1974 BAYERN MUNICH WERE THE EUROPEAN CUP WINNERS, BEATING ATLETICO MADRID 4-0 AFTER A REPLAY. WATCHED BY GERD MULLER, SKIPPER FRANZ BECKENBAUER HOLDS UP THE TROPHY. NOT LONG AFTERWARDS THEY SHARED IN AN EVEN GREATER TRIUMPH — WEST GERMANY'S WORLD CUP WIN...

END

WHO's the twenty third man on the pitch in every soccer game? The referee, of course! He's been called "the man in the middle"—although the fans often have other names for the chap with the whistle!

It's no fun being a top referee who, as the man in charge, has to make split-second decisions during a game—and stick to them, whatever the players and the fans think about it. Referees are as dedicated to the game as the players they have to control on the field. No man has proved this more than Jack Taylor (below), the big, genial Wolverhampton referee, whom Don Revie regards as the finest in the game—"a man respected by everyone in football." England's team boss, former player and manager of Leeds United, wouldn't praise any man so highly unless he was worthy of it, and Don Revie meant every word.

Jack Taylor, master-

From park pitches to mighty stadiums, football could not be played without the referee, for . . .

HE'S THE MAN IN CHARGE!

butcher in the Midlands, is famous throughout the soccer world. Certainly no referee has "whistled" in more matches and in more countries. He has travelled to every part of the world as one of the leading FIFA referees. On one of his trips abroad he officiated at matches in China and Hong Kong, where he held a coaching course for local refs.

He was appointed to the F.A. referees' list in 1957 and quickly proved himself a worthy "man in the middle." Since then he has officiated at the Amateur Cup Final (1962), the F.A. Cup Final (1966), when Everton achieved a magnificent 3-2 victory over Sheffield Wednesday; and the greatest honour of all—the World Cup Final in 1974. Jack Taylor was on the referees' panel for the 1966 and 1970 World Cup tournaments and then in 1974 he was chosen to take charge of the Final in Munich between West Germany and

On his way to Blackpool, Jack Taylor (left), calls at the Football League offices and meets an official.

At the Blackpool ground he enjoys a cup of tea with one of his linesmen (centre).

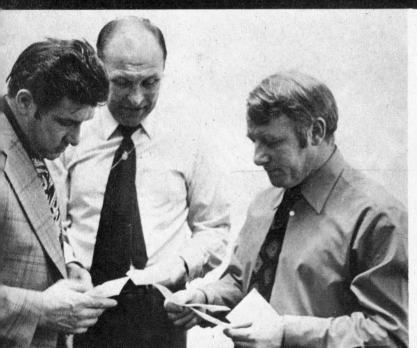

Blackpool are playing Manchester United so Jack has a quick look at the team sheets with the rival managers.

Back in the ref's room, he checks the team sheets.

Holland, the first British referee to "take" the World Cup Final since George Reader way back in 1950.

It was the most important game Jack had ever refereed but he came through the ordeal with flying colours. In the first minute of that terrific battle Johann Cruyff, the Dutch captain, was brought down in the penalty-area. Without a moment's hesitation Jack Taylor pointed to the penalty spot. It was a brave thing to do. As one Continental reporter wrote: " Only an English referee would have had the courage to give that penalty." But then Jack Taylor has never shirked responsibility. For the remainder of the Final, which, you may remember, was won 2–1 by the West Germans, his control of the game and his firm but fair decisions earned the admiration and the applause of the whole world. Yet, of course, to Jack Taylor it was just another game among the hundreds he has refereed. So those of us who know him were not surprised that he was so successful on the greatest day of his life as the "man in charge". He's one of the best in the business.

chap on the extreme left is Jack's friend.

Long before the majority of the fans arrive at the ground, Jack takes a walk over the pitch on which he is to referee.

Now it's time to take the field with his linesmen. "Good old Jack!"

The moment the fans are waiting for—the toss-up, with the two captains, Willie Morgan and Glyn James.

MATCH-DAY

IN this special 6-page feature we have tried to give you some idea of a typical Saturday afternoon in the refereeing life of Jack Taylor who was due to referee a match at Blackpool. Like all the top whistlers he must be prepared to travel all over the country for League and Cup games and this often means that he leaves his home on Friday and does not return until early on Sunday morning. Then, of course, there are mid-week games and special appointments overseas. So you see it's a full, busy and hectic life. Then you must realise that he has to keep himself in tip-top physical condition, which means regular training. No referee can expect to keep up with the pace of modern football unless he is really fit. Players earn fabulous money but not referees—that is why they must be dedicated to the game and love the job.

How would you like to be called out in the early hours of the morning to travel to the ground of the club where you are to referee a game that afternoon? It often happens

to men like Jack Taylor. You see, the referee is the only man who can give a final decision on whether a ground is fit for play following heavy rain or in snowy or icy weather. If it is possible he must give his decision in time to notify the visiting team before they leave for the match. He is also the only man who can call off a match at the last minute if he finds the pitch unplayable. Even if the two club managers feel that the game should be played he can still " out-vote " them. Another of his duties is to make a report on every match at which he officiates, and this includes full details of any bookings he has made during the game. It may be, too, that he will be called to give evidence at the F.A. enquiry when a player appeals against his booking. So, you see, the referee is most definitely the " man in charge ".

Now it's Jack Taylor in action but he's not giving a victory sign (above), nor cheering a goal. He's the ref—not a fan. (Below) He's having a word with Gerry Daly of Manchester United, but it's obviously something to smile about.

ROAD TO THE TOP

YOU may have wondered how a man becomes a top referee. Well, most of them

JACK'S GREATEST MOMENT!

HERE'S a memorable shot of the start of the greatest game Jack Taylor ever refereed— the 1974 World Cup Final at Munich. Surrounded by cameramen he is asking Johann Cruyff, captain of Holland, to choose "Heads" or "Tails" watched by the two linesmen and Franz Beckenbauer, the famous skipper of West Germany. The tension inside the great Olympic Stadium was terrific but England's ace ref was as cool as a cucumber. To him this was just a game of football and he was the man in charge. Within a minute of the kick-off Cruyff was fouled in the penalty-box. Instantly Jack pointed to the penalty-spot, and the Dutch opened the scoring. It had never happened before in a World Cup Final but Jack Taylor never hesitated in his decision. For the rest of that great game he kept a firm control and earned praise from everyone in the stadium, including all the players—winners and losers.

start in local junior football after passing the provisional examination. The future is up to the individual. After more studies and exams he can rise to the next grade and the next until, if he is proficient enough, he is appointed to the F.A. list of senior linesmen. Did you realise that all the men who race up and down the touchlines are refs in their own right? But having reached that stage, it may be some years before a linesman is up-graded to the official referees' list and, of course, only a few ever receive the coveted FIFA badge, which means they can take charge of top internationals.

The "Jack Taylors" of football can be counted in tens, not hundreds. Then you must remember that the F.A. decree that a referee must retire at the age of 47 even though he may still be among the best in the game. It sounds ridiculous, doesn't it, but that's the rule.

One of the finest referees during the past ten or twelve years was Gordon Hill, Leicester headmaster. Throughout the football world he was known as "a players' ref", not because he showed any favours on the field but because he went about his difficult job quietly and fairly and firmly. He seldom had any trouble during a game because the players knew he was in complete control and would stand no nonsense from anyone. Many's the time that Gordon Hill congratulated players after a game. He appreciated good football and the players respected him for his attitude. He was the man in charge—the gaffer, but not a

Two "no nonsense" snaps of Jack Taylor during the Blackpool–Manchester United game (above and right). Then, to finish our story, Jack follows the players off the field.

dictator. The players were friends and not enemies and, like Jack Taylor, the fans admired him, too.

Unfortunately, he has now had to retire, having reached the age of 47 and his last big match was the 1975 League Cup Final. It was a sad day for Gordon Hill —but an even sadder day for English football, players and fans alike.

By the way, have you ever wondered what referees do when they are not "whistling"?

Well, Ron Crabb from Exeter is a prison officer; some have shops, while Pat Partridge, from Co. Durham, has a flourishing dairy farm. You must remember that no man can make a living as a referee—it's a part-time job, and it ends all too soon for most of them.

It won't be long now before Jack Taylor is forced to hang-up his boots and his whistle at the end of a wonderful refereeing career. **Football will certainly miss him . . .**

Well done, Jack Taylor, England's No. 1 ref! We're all proud of you!

TERRACE TITTERS

NIPPER

LAWRENCE, YOU LOOK DISGUSTINGLY UNTIDY! YOU MIGHT AT LEAST HAVE PUT A COMB THROUGH YOUR HAIR AND PULLED UP YOUR SOCKS! THINK OF THE CLUB'S IMAGE!

NIPPER LAWRENCE, WHO PLAYED FOR FIRST DIVISION BLACKPORT ROVERS, WAS A YOUNG BACK-STREET ORPHAN WHO HAD HAD TO MAKE HIS OWN WAY IN THE GAME. JUST AS THE PLAYERS WERE GOING OUT FOR A LEAGUE MATCH AGAINST THAMESBANK, A HAUGHTY SNEERING VOICE ROUSED NIPPER'S TEMPER...

FLAMIN' NORAH! THIS IS A FOOTBALL MATCH, NOT A FASHION PARADE!

HOW YOU LOOK DOESN'T HAVE MUCH TO DO WITH WINNING A GAME!

NIPPER WAS STILL BOILING AS HE RAN ON TO THE PITCH WITH HIS PAL MIKE BATESON...

THAT LIONEL DUKES! ALWAYS BRAGGING ABOUT HIS MILLIONAIRE UNCLE! HE ACTS AS IF HE WAS RUNNING THE CLUB, YET HE'S ONLY A GLORIFIED OFFICE-BOY!

I SUPPOSE YOU CAN'T HELP BEING OFFENSIVE, HAVING BEEN DRAGGED UP IN THE DOCKS! I SOMETIMES FORGET THAT EVERYONE HASN'T HAD MY ADVANTAGE OF BEING WELL EDUCATED BY A RICH UNCLE!

BLOWED IF I CAN THINK WHY THE CHAIRMAN GAVE THE SNOB A JOB IN THE FIRST PLACE!

OUR CHAIRMAN'S A BIT OF A SNOB HIMSELF! I RECKON HE'S IMPRESSED BY LIONEL'S TALES OF HIS POSH UNCLE, HIS UPBRINGING AND TOFFEE-NOSED FAMILY! DON'T LET IT WORRY YOU!

BUT NIPPER FAILED TO TAKE HIS PAL'S ADVICE...

FOUL!

PHEEP!

FREE-KICK TO THAMESBANK!

COOL IT, NIPPER!

THUD!

17

19

SIR JULIUS DUKES! N-NOT LIONEL'S RICH UNCLE?

THAT EXPLAINS IT! FROM ALL YOUR STUCK-UP NEPHEW HAS BRAGGED ABOUT YOU, YOU'RE ONE OF THOSE PEOPLE WHO THINK THAT EVERYONE ELSE HAS TO JUMP OUT OF YOUR WAY, OR GET KNOCKED DOWN!

I'M AFRAID I DON'T UNDERSTAND THE REASON FOR THAT OUTBURST! WHAT'S MY REVOLTING NEPHEW BEEN UP TO? YOU'D ALL THREE BETTER GET INTO THE CAR AND EXPLAIN!

A FEW MORNINGS LATER, WHEN THE PLAYERS WERE ABOUT TO START A TRAINING SESSION, LIONEL RUSHED UP TO THEM ...

MY UNCLE IS VISITING BLACKPORT AND HE'S ASKED TO MEET YOU ALL! WE'RE TO BE AT THE DOCKS WHEN HIS SHIP BERTHS, SO I'VE BOOKED HIM A SUITE AT THE *IMPERIAL HOTEL.* WE'LL ENTERTAIN HIM TO LUNCH THERE!

FOR SOME REASON HE HAS SPECIALLY ASKED TO MEET YOU, LAWRENCE, SO FOR GOODNESS SAKE DO YOUR BEST NOT TO LET THE SIDE DOWN! TURN UP LOOKING CLEAN AND DECENT!

LIONEL WAS ALMOST BURSTING WITH CONCEIT WHEN THEY ALL GATHERED AT THE DOCKS ...

THAT'S BOUND TO BE MY UNCLE'S SHIP! IT'S THE BIGGEST IN THE PORT!

THEN HE HEARD A RASPING VOICE THAT SENT SHIVERS DOWN HIS SPINE...

BELAY THERE, SHIP-MATES! IS ONE OF YOU SMART GENTS ME LITTLE NEPHEW LIONEL DUKES?

AFTER HEARING NIPPER'S STORY SIR JULIUS HAD DECIDED TO TEACH HIS NEPHEW A LESSON, AND HAD MADE A FEW CHANGES IN HIS APPEARANCE...

OH, NO! I DON'T BELIEVE IT! YOU CAN'T BE UNCLE JULIUS!

'COURSE I AM! AND YOU AIN'T CHANGED A BIT! STILL THE SAME PIE-FACED, TOFFEE-NOSED LITTLE SWAB YOU ALWAYS WAS!

ARE ALL THESE 'ERE POSH TOFFS YER MATES THEN, YOUNG LINO? COME UP IN THE WORLD SINCE THE OLD DAYS, AIN'CHA?

I 'OPE THAT GETTING PALLY WITH ALL THESE TOFFS AIN'T MADE YER ASHAMED OF YER 'UMBLE BEGINNINGS? 'OW'S YER DAD KEEPIN'? AIN'T SEEN THE OLD BOY FER YEARS! STILL A RAG-AND-BONE MAN IS HE?

HELP ME! HE'S MAD! MY FATHER NEVER DID THAT FOR A LIVING!

LIONEL TRIED TO ESCAPE, BUT KERRY GRABBED HIM...

WHERE WE GONNER 'AVE THIS NOSH THEN?

I CAN'T STAND ANY MORE OF THIS! I'M OFF!

HE'S YOUR UNCLE, SO YOU STAY AND HELP ENTERTAIN HIM!

TO LIONEL'S HORROR, HIS UNCLE INSISTED ON BRINGING THE HORSE...

COULDN'T LEAVE THE 'ORSE BE'IND, COULD I, SHIP-MATES?

IMPERIAL

A POSH LOOKING CAFF YOU BROUGHT ME TO, LINO! I 'OPE THEY SERVES DECENT GRUB, LIKE COW-'EELS AND TRIPE!

LOOK HERE, MY MAN, YOU CAN'T COME IN HERE, AND YOU CAN'T LEAVE THIS ANIMAL HERE!

LIONEL'S TERROR MOUNTED AS HIS UNCLE SWEPT THE DOORMAN ASIDE AND MET A SHOCKED HEAD WAITER...

I'M **NOT** YOUR MAN! I'M GOIN' IN! YOU JUST KEEP AN EYE ON THE 'ORSE!

I'M SORRY, SIR, WE'RE—ER—FULLY BOOKED!

WHAT DO YOU MEAN—MY FRIENDS AND I CAN'T EAT HERE? PULL YOURSELF TOGETHER, MAN—I OWN THE PLACE!

SIR JULIUS! I AM TERRIBLY SORRY, SIR! OH, DEAR...

JUST MAKE YOURSELVES AT HOME WHILE I HAVE A BATH AND CHANGE INTO SOME DECENT CLOTHES! AS FOR YOU, LIONEL—TAKE THAT HORSE ROUND THE BACK AND SEE THAT IT GETS A BUCKET OF WATER AND SOME OATS!

WHEN SIR JULIUS HAD GONE, NIPPER AND HIS FRIENDS TURNED ON LIONEL IN GLEE...

YOUR UNCLE WAS SENDING YOU UP!

AND SERVE YOU RIGHT! I HOPE IT'S TAUGHT YOU A LESSON!

HA, HA, HAA!

SIR JULIUS HAD MADE ADVANCE ARRANGEMENTS TO ENTERTAIN HIS GUESTS LAVISHLY...

I AM SURE WE ALL APPRECIATE YOUR LITTLE JOKE, SIR JULIUS! MAY WE NOW USE THIS OPPORTUNITY TO DISCUSS THE MATTER OF YOUR LENDING FINANCIAL SUPPORT TO BLACKPORT?

IT WAS NO JOKE! WHEN I LEARNED HOW MY NEPHEW HAD BEEN BEHAVING I WAS SO DISGUSTED THAT I ALMOST DECIDED TO HAVE NOTHING TO DO WITH THE CLUB!

HOWEVER, HAVING HAD THE OPPORTUNITY TO MEET THE REST OF YOU, ESPECIALLY NIPPER LAWRENCE AND THIS CHARMING YOUNG LADY, I'VE CHANGED MY MIND! YOU'LL HAVE TO PROMISE TO SEE TO IT THAT LIONEL BEHAVES HIMSELF IN FUTURE, AND IN RETURN I WILL PROMISE BLACKPORT ALL THE SUPPORT IT NEEDS FROM ME!

AND AT BLACKPORT'S NEXT HOME GAME, NIPPER CELEBRATED WITH A FANTASTIC PERFORMANCE...

GOAL!

THAT'S NIPPER'S HAT-TRICK!

WHAT A GREAT PLAYER!

NO SUPPORTER WAS MORE PLEASED THAN SIR JULIUS...

IT'S PLAYERS LIKE NIPPER THAT HAVE MADE BLACKPORT A TOP TEAM, EH, LIONEL?

ER, Y-YES, UNCLE! WELL PLAYED, NIPPER LAWRENCE!

The End.

JIMMY GREAVES

SOCCER

STANLEY MATTHEWS

JOHNNY HAYNES

THE word "century" is usually connected with cricket the scoring of a "ton" 100 runs in an innings. **But there are many interesting stories of "centurions" in soccer.** Nothing whatever to do with Julius Caesar's fearsome gladiators (there was no football in their day!), nor are we referring to players who have reached the ripe old age of 100 years. Then what? Well, let's take a look at some of these amazing soccer centurions.

You know, of course, that only three men have achieved a century of caps for England Billy Wright, Bobby Charlton and Bobby Moore, but so far as we can trace only one player has ever scored 100 goals in international football, the immortal Brazilian ace Pele. It may be a long time before that record target is beaten.

When it comes to goals, however, there have been many record-breaking centurions in League football. Not many cricketers have ever hit more than 400 runs in an innings and very few footballers have topped four tons during their career. The record is held by Arthur Rowley, now manager of Southend United, with a total of 434 goals in 619 League games for West Bromwich Albion, Fulham, Leicester City and Shrewsbury.

This super sharpshooter reached his first and second centuries with Leicester and then went on to his third and fourth with Shrewsbury. In all matches with his four clubs he hit the net more than 500 times and only one other player ever achieved a 5-ton total. He was Jimmy McGrory, who topped 550 Cup and League goals during a remarkable 16-year career with Celtic, setting a Scottish League record with 410 goals.

Arthur Rowley and his brother John, who was a shooting star with Manchester United Championship and Cup-winning teams both before and after the war, achieved a fantastic record. Both scored their 200th League goal **ON THE SAME DAY,** 22nd October, 1956! Arthur hit his second century for Leicester City against Fulham, while John got his 200th for Plymouth Argyle at Barnsley 12 minutes behind Arthur!

Jimmy Greaves earned top billing as a goal-buster. The cheeky, chirpy little Cockney hit his first century with Chelsea in December, 1960, before his 21st birthday; topped his second century three years later with Tottenham Hotspur and, later, with West Ham, reached a total of 357 First Division goals. In all Jimmy collected 492 goals in all matches, including 44 in 58 England internationals, before he retired. Pity he couldn't have stayed long

CENTURIONS

BOBBY CHARLTON

JIMMY DICKINSON

enough to hit 500!

We were all disappointed, too, when Bobby Charlton retired in 1973 to become manager of Preston North End with 198 League goals for Manchester United just two short of his double century. But in August, 1974, Bobby decided to don his shooting boots once more and in Preston's fourth match of the season collected his second goal in less than a week and so joined the "Double Ton-up Club". But that's not the complete story of Bobby "Centurion" Charlton, whose total of 106 England caps was a record until his pal Bobby Moore beat it. He and brother Jack each passed a total of 600 League matches—with one club. Bobby appeared in a club record 606 League matches for Manchester United and big Jack set the Leeds United "most appearances" record with 629. **That "double" in itself must be an all-time record for centurions.**

But one famous player reached and passed his *seventh* century of Football League games with his one and only club—Jimmy Dickinson, who made 764 appearances for Portsmouth in 19 consecutive seasons. It's a colossal total, isn't it? Sir Stanley Matthews also topped 700 League appearances 701 to be exact but not only did the "Wizard of Dribble" play for two clubs,

Stoke City and Blackpool, he made his last appearance a few days after his 50th birthday. However, that, too, is an incredible "half-ton" record.

Goalies have achieved their centuries, too. Sam Bartram played in 579 League games for Charlton Athletic a club and League record; Bert Trautmann, the former German prisoner-of-war, still holds the Manchester City record with 508 League appearances, and Ted Ditchburn held Spurs' record with 418 before he was passed by Pat Jennings.

There was a time when fans had the chance to cheer their team's "ton-up" goals total in one season. In 1956 57 all four Champions 1st. 2nd and both 3rd Divisions topped 100 in the "goals for" column. The following season three teams in the First Division and two in the Second all scored 100 or more goals. One of them was Manchester City who set up an incredible record. Although they scored 104 goals they had 100 scored against them a unique "double century".

So, you see, cricket doesn't have all the sporting centurions. Soccer's "ton-up" boys have made history, too, including Johnny Haynes who played in 600 games for Fulham. scored 148 League goals and became the first £100 a week footballer in 1961.

Know-All

He's Soccer's Mister Big-Head! See If You Can Catch Him Out.

ANSWERS BELOW

GREAT ACTION FROM HIGHFIELD ROAD, COVENTRY, AS DON GIVENS OF QUEEN'S PARK RANGERS (DARK SHIRT), RACES AFTER THE BALL, CLOSELY FOLLOWED BY CITY'S JIMMY HOLMES. ALTHOUGH ON OPPOSITE SIDES IN THIS GAME, BOTH MEN PLAY FOR THE SAME INTERNATIONAL TEAM — EIRE!

HERE'S ONE OF THE TOP MIDFIELD MEN IN THE GAME — CHELSEA'S DAVID HAY. DO YOU REMEMBER HIS SUPER PERFORMANCES FOR SCOTLAND IN THE 1974 WORLD CUP TOURNAMENT?

A BIG FAVOURITE WITH THE SUNDERLAND FANS IS THEIR BRILLIANT STRIKER, 'POP' ROBSON, WHO HELPED THE CLUB ACHIEVE GLORY WHEN THEY WON THE F.A. CUP IN 1973!

GUARDING THE GOAL IN PREPARATION FOR A CORNER-KICK IS DUNDEE'S ACE DEFENDER, TOMMY GEMMELL. TOMMY'S ENJOYED A WONDERFUL SOCCER CAREER, AND WON A HOST OF HONOURS WITH RANGERS, ONE OF HIS FORMER CLUBS!

I'M GOING TO AYRESOME PARK SOON TO SEE MIDDLESBROUGH IN ACTION. ARE YOU COMING?

I'D LIKE TO, KNOW-ALL, BUT 'BORO DON'T PLAY THERE!

Answers: 1. Right, Know-All. 2. Good—correct again. 3. Wrong, Know-All. 'Pop' Robson was still a West Ham player when Sunderland won the F.A. Cup in 1973. 4. Incorrect. Tommy Gemmell was once a star with Celtic. 5. Right, Know-All. Middlesbrough's ground is called Ayresome Park.

26

THE TRANSFER TREE

Fortunes have changed hands since the transfer tree produced its first £1,000 leaf in 1905.

£55,000

When Denis Law joined Manchester City from Huddersfield in March, 1960, for £55,000, he became the first £50,000-plus footballer.

£53,000

John Charles, "The Gentle Giant" of Wales, left Leeds in 1957 to play in Italy but in 1962 United bought him back—for a fee of £53,000.

£56,000

Paddy Crerand's move from Celtic to Manchester United in February, 1963, set a new British transfer record of £56,000—a costly Scot.

£100,000

Chelsea paid Sheffield United £100,000 in 1967 for Alan Birchenall (second from left). He later moved to Palace and Leicester for the same fee.

£100,000

Mick Jones also left Sheffield United in 1967 for a £100,000 fee. Leeds United have never regretted signing this sharp-shooting star.

£110,000

Alan Ball scores his first goal for Everton after his £110,000 transfer from Blackpool (Aug. 1966). He cost Arsenal £220,000 in Dec. 1971.

£150,000

Everton paid Nottingham Forest £150,000 for Henry Newton in Oct. 1970. Three years later he moved to Derby Co. for £100,000.

£170,000

Steve Kember had played in nearly 250 games for Crystal Palace when he was signed by Chelsea in Sept. 1971, for £170,000, their record fee.

£150,000

Allan Clarke (on the left below with Billy Bremner) joined Leicester from Fulham (1968) for £150,000; later he went to Leeds for £165,000.

£200,000

Martin Peters heads his first goal for Spurs in March, 1970, after his transfer from West Ham in a £200,000 deal—the first ever in Britain.

£200,000

Rodney Marsh (right, below) signs for Manchester City in March, 1972, after Queen's Park Rangers had agreed to transfer him for £200,000.

£200,000

Another member of the "club for £200,000 stars" is wee Lou Macari, who moved from Celtic to Manchester United for that sum in Jan. 1973.

£250,000

Duncan McKenzie has become an England squad-man since joining Leeds United from Nottingham Forest in Aug. 1974, for a £250,000 fee.

£250,000

The first ever £250,000 fee was paid by Derby Co. to Leicester, in Aug. 1972, for their star defender England Under-23 cap, David Nish.

£275,000

Peter Osgood signs for Southampton in March, 1974. "Saints" paid Chelsea a fee of £275,000 for their 100-goal England striker.

£350,000

Everton set a new record in Feb. 1974, when they signed Bob Latchford from Birmingham in a cash and two player deal worth at least £350,000.

£300,000

Six months later Everton took Martin Dobson from Burnley for £300,000. It was the first time one player had moved for such a huge sum.

£500,000

£750,000

£1m

The transfer tree continues to grow. In the years between 1960 and 1974 fees have risen from £50,000 to £350,000 as the value of soccer's golden stars has gone higher and higher. What of the future? Shall we see the record doubled, or will the tree begin to die back? Who can tell?

The Internationals

SCOTLAND

BILLY BREMNER
Leeds

TOMMY HUTCHISON
Coventry

JOE JORDAN
Leeds

PETER LORIMER
Leeds

SANDY JARDINE
Rangers

SUB.

HE'S ALWAYS ON THE SIDELINES!

SATURDAY AFTERNOON, IN THE BIGGLESWICK WANDERERS' DRESSING-ROOM...

CHANGING INTO THESE FOOTBALL TOGS IS JUST A MOCKERY! I NEVER GET A GAME!

AW! STOP MOANING, DUGGIE DRIBBLE! YOUR CHANCE WILL COME!

I HOPE NOT!

HEH, HEH! I'LL MAKE SURE IT DOES — ACCIDENTALLY ON PURPOSE!

LIMBER UP, LADS!

TOSS

SOAP

EEEE! YOW-W!

OOPH!

GLOOP!

GLUB

SKID

BAM

THANKS FOR BREAKING MY FALL, SUB! NO HARM DONE!

HUH! YOU SPEAK FOR YOURSELF, MATE!

UGGLE-UGGLE-UGGLE—

OKAY, LADS! TIME TO GO OUT ON THE PITCH! GRAB A BALL EACH FOR KICKING-IN PRACTICE!

THIS IS MY CHANCE! I'LL MAKE SURE OF A GAME, YET!

HEH HEH!

THINKS:- HEH HEH!-

BAM

OO-OOO

ANYONE CAN MIS-KICK A BALL DURING PRACTICE!

NUMBER SEVEN'LL DO FOR A START... HERE GOES!

HEY, BERT! YOUR BOOT-LACE IS UNDONE!

THUD

THANKS FOR NOTICING IT...!

...A THING LIKE THIS COULD RESULT IN A NASTY ACCIDENT FOR SOMEBODY!

OO-ER! I'VE CLOBBERED A COPPER!

THUD

SQUELCH

OUCH!

LINE UP FOR THE KICK-OFF, LADS! GET THOSE PRACTICE-BALLS OFF THE PITCH!

GRR-R! ALLOW ME TO DO THAT!

THROB

SNARL!

GULP! IT'S TIME I WASN'T HERE!

BUT BEFORE DUGGIE COULD REACH SAFETY...

TAKE THAT!

AND THAT!

AND THAT!

BAM

THUD

HELP! SOME-BODY CALL A POLICEMAN TO DEAL WITH A CRAZY ONE!

BIFF

AFTER THE BOMBARDMENT...

BAH! NOW WE NEED A SUBSTITUTE FOR A SUBSTITUTE!

HO, HO! THE SUB'S BEEN SUNK!

GURGLE!

THANK GOODNESS!

The Title No British Team Has Won! The EUROPEAN CHAMPIONSHIP

YOU **may not believe this, but it's true.** The only European title that has never been won by a team representing England, Scotland, Wales or Northern Ireland is the European Championship, previously known as the Nations Cup. Nor has any of the four Home countries ever reached the Final—at least, not yet, for the Final of the 1974–76 competition will not be played until next summer.

The European Championship is run on similar lines to the World Cup with the competing countries divided into groups playing home and away games, followed by Quarter-finals and Semi-finals, the whole competition covering a period of two years. Also, like the World Cup, there is a four-year break between each European Final. The first Nations Cup tournament, as it was then known, kicked-off in 1958, but only 18 countries showed any interest. The four British Football Associations did not enter for various reasons. Eventually Russia and Yugoslavia reached the Final played in Paris. The Russians, who were given a walk-over in the Quarter-finals when Spain withdrew, won the trophy 2–1 after extra-time.

When the next "Nations" began in 1962 the entry list had risen to 32, including England, Ireland and Wales, with the Scots still remaining on the side-lines. But the other British sides didn't proceed very far. England were knocked out in the First Round by France and Wales by Hungary. The Irishmen reached the Second Round before being k.o'd by the Spaniards, who went on to win the Cup from the holders, Russia, in Madrid.

In 1966 UEFA changed the system, introducing groups as in the World Cup. One of these groups consisted of the four British countries playing home and away games against each other. This meant that only the winners of the group could move into the Quarter-finals—and that was England. It was unfair on the Scots, the Welsh and the Irish and the idea lasted for only that 1966–68 competition. As it was the England squad, led by Sir Alf Ramsey and skipper Bobby Moore, with most of the World Cup winning side, reached the Semi-finals only to be knocked out by Yugoslavia. England beat Russia for third place honours and Italy beat Yugoslavia in the Rome final 2–0, after a 1–1 draw.

For the 1970–72 European Championship contest the four Home countries were drawn in different groups but it made little difference to the eventual results. Only England reached the Quarter-finals—and went no farther in the competition. They met their old World Cup rivals from West Germany. The first-leg was at Wembley—but this was no repeat of the 1966 World Cup Final. Yes, it was a great game, but the Germans romped away with a 3–1 victory. There was still the second-leg to come, in Berlin, but it was too much to expect England to win by at least three goals. They put up a gallant fight but could only share a goalless draw, so Beckenbauer took his wonderful team into the Semi-finals. They beat Belgium and lined up against the Russians in the Brussels Final. It was the Soviet side's third Final appearance in four European Championship Finals but this time they were outplayed by a brilliant combination of all the soccer arts. Handsome Franz Beckenbauer proudly accepted the trophy after leading his side to a 3–0 win—with two of the goals coming from that ace sharpshooter, Gerd "Bomber" Muller.

That wonderful triumph earned the West German skipper Franz Beckenbauer the "Golden Ball" award as European Footballer of the Year and two years later he achieved his greatest honour—as captain of the West German World Cup winners. Next summer he could make it a golden hat-trick by leading his wonder-side to their third major trophy triumph in the space of four years and their second European Championship. The 1974–76 tournament began way back in August, 1974, with all four of the British countries taking part. **When will one of them earn the title of "European Kings"?**

1960 — The first European
Championship Final (above).
Russia beat Yugoslavia 2-1.

Left: Action from the 1964
Final in Madrid when Spain
defeated the holders, USSR.

Bobby Moore (six) cannot stop
Yugoslavia knocking out England
in 1968.

Above: Anastasi (dark shirt) nets Italy's second goal in the 1968 Final v. Yugoslavia. Right: Happy skipper Facchetti with the Cup.

1972: England lose in the Quarter-Finals to West Germany at Wembley.

England's only goal in that 3-1 defeat,
scored by Lee (arm up).

1972 Final—West Germany 3, Russia 0. Here,
Muller nets the first. Below: Delighted Beckenbauer and Netzer with the super trophy.

THESE BOOTS

A step by step photo feature on how football boots are made

were made for FOOTBALL!

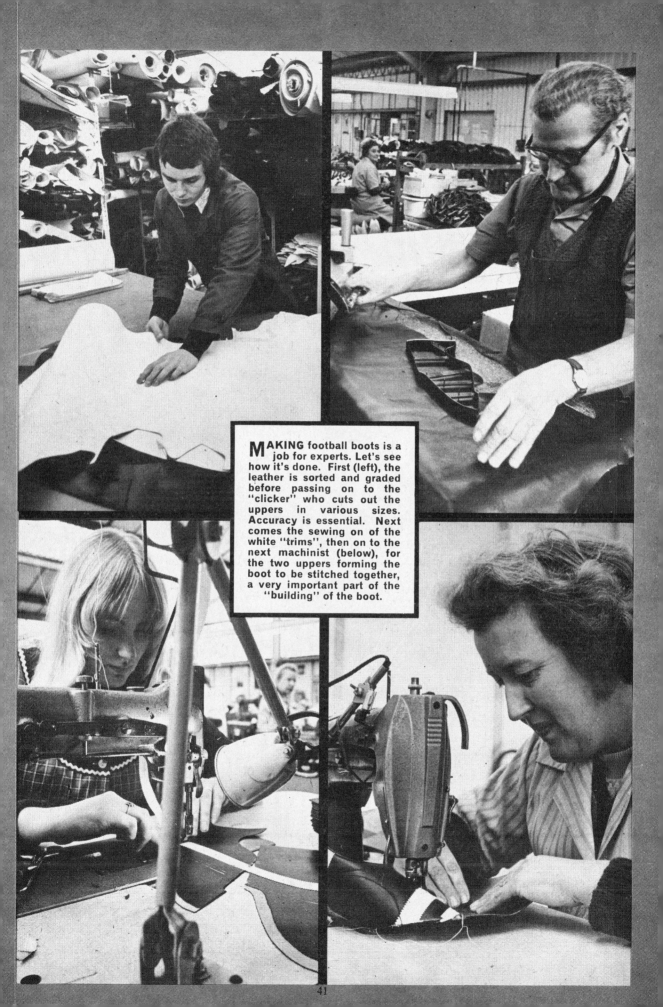

MAKING football boots is a job for experts. Let's see how it's done. First (left), the leather is sorted and graded before passing on to the "clicker" who cuts out the uppers in various sizes. Accuracy is essential. Next comes the sewing on of the white "trims", then on to the next machinist (below), for the two uppers forming the boot to be stitched together, a very important part of the "building" of the boot.

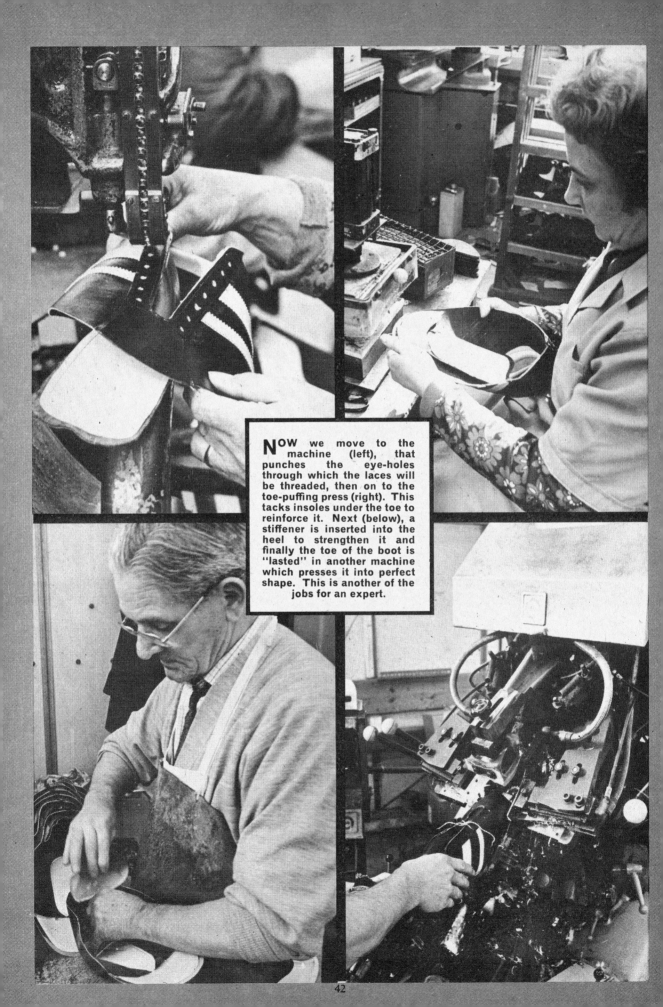

NOW we move to the machine (left), that punches the eye-holes through which the laces will be threaded, then on to the toe-puffing press (right). This tacks insoles under the toe to reinforce it. Next (below), a stiffener is inserted into the heel to strengthen it and finally the toe of the boot is "lasted" in another machine which presses it into perfect shape. This is another of the jobs for an expert.

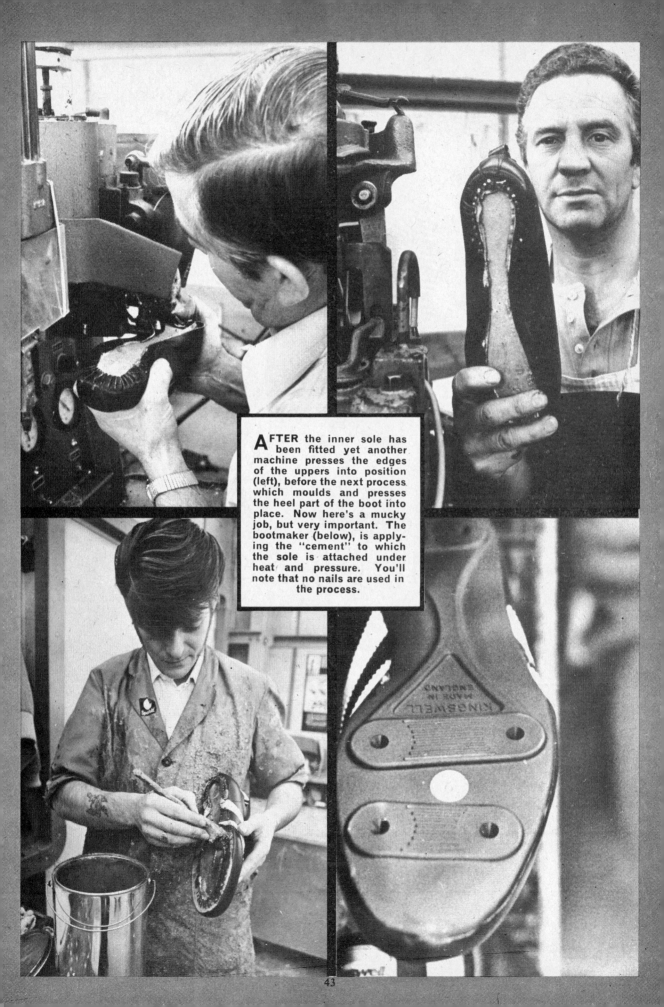

AFTER the inner sole has been fitted yet another machine presses the edges of the uppers into position (left), before the next process which moulds and presses the heel part of the boot into place. Now here's a mucky job, but very important. The bootmaker (below), is applying the "cement" to which the sole is attached under heat and pressure. You'll note that no nails are used in the process.

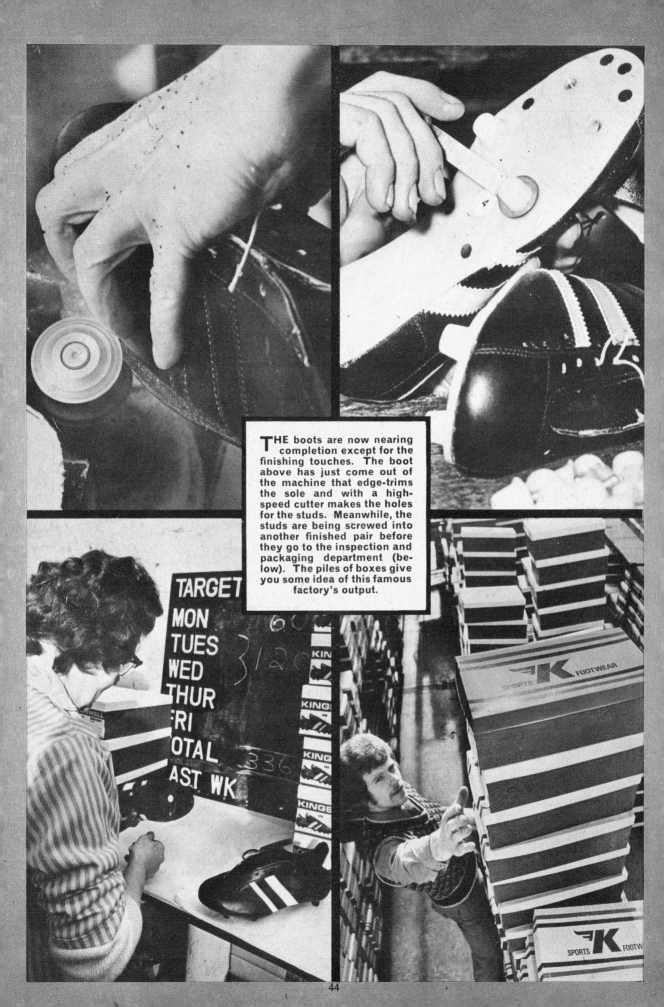

THE boots are now nearing completion except for the finishing touches. The boot above has just come out of the machine that edge-trims the sole and with a high-speed cutter makes the holes for the studs. Meanwhile, the studs are being screwed into another finished pair before they go to the inspection and packaging department (below). The piles of boxes give you some idea of this famous factory's output.

Like all top soccer stars Colin Todd, Derby County's brilliant England international, would agree that no player can take chances with his footer boots. Only the best are good enough —and that's why the factory you have been privileged to visit take so much care in the boots they produce. But remember, YOU can wear the same type of boots as your favourite stars. They are made in all sizes—from schoolboy to international.

Royal's Rangers

ON A GROUND SOGGY WITH SPRING RAIN, CAXFORD RANGERS, WHO WERE KNOWN AS ROYAL'S RANGERS AFTER THEIR POPULAR MANAGER BEN ROYAL, HAD BATTLED THEIR WAY TO WHAT SEEMED AN ALMOST CERTAIN WIN...

THERE'S ONLY FOUR MINUTES LEFT TO PLAY... AND CAXFORD ARE ONE UP!

JUST KEEP THE BALL AWAY FROM BRANTON FOR A FEW MINUTES, RANGERS, AND WE'RE BOUND TO WIN!

BUT BRANTON ATHLETIC, AND THEIR STAR STRIKER IN PARTICULAR, WERE FIGHTING BACK WITH EVERYTHING THEY HAD...

TERRY'S GOT IT! COME ON, BRANTON!

HE'S ONLY GOT ONE BACK AND THE GOALIE TO BEAT!

BUT THERE WAS NO NERVOUSNESS ON THE FACE OF CAXFORD'S RIGHT-BACK, BIG JIM BLACKER, AS DANGER SWEPT TOWARDS HIM...

IT MUST BE THE EQUALISER! BOOT IT IN, BRANTON!

LOOK AT BIG JIM WAITING FOR 'IM! HE ISN'T RATTLED... HE NEVER IS!

HEADING THE BALL WASN'T JIM'S STRONGEST POINT OF PLAY, BUT THIS TIME....

TACKLE HIM, JIM! TAKE THE..... HEY! WHAT'S HE DOING?

HE'S GOING TO TRY A HIGH LOB... I'M SURE HE IS!

THE BURLY FULL-BACK HAD GUESSED RIGHT, BUT LUCK WAS NOT WITH HIM...

JIM'S GOT HIS HEAD TO IT! HE'S... OH, MY GOSH!

HE'S HEADED IT INTO HIS OWN GOAL! WE'VE EQUALISED!

THANKS VERY MUCH, RANGERS! HA, HA!

DON'T BLAME YOURSELF, JIM. IT CAN HAPPEN TO ANYONE!

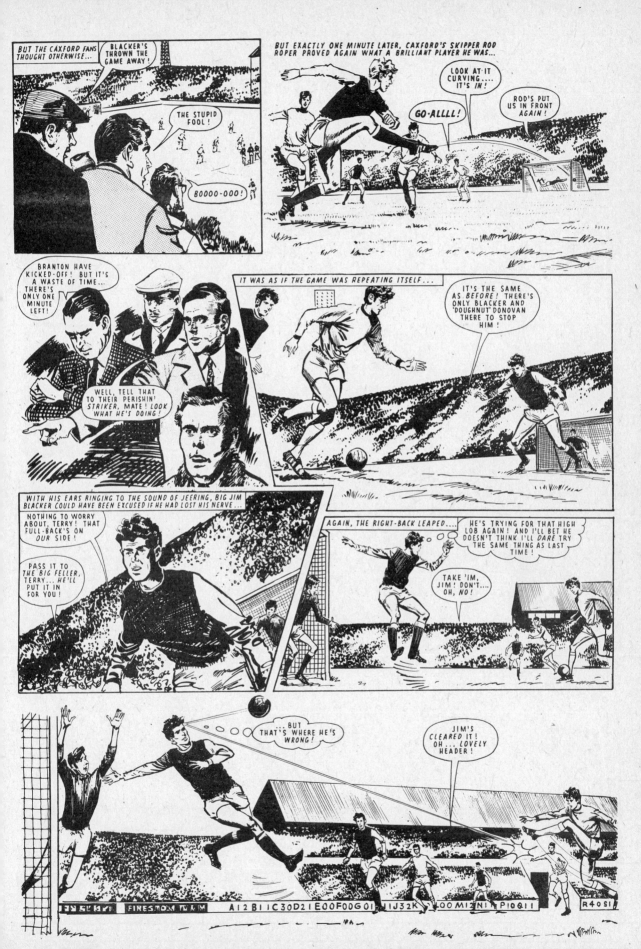

47

WHEN THE PLANE TOUCHED DOWN...

WELCOME CAXFORD RANGERS

WOW! WHAT A WELCOME! ALL **THIS** JUST FOR **US**!

THEY MUST THINK WE'RE A BUNCH OF PRINCES, FOR PETE'S SAKE!

PORTLY PRESIDENT MENTEREZ COULDN'T HAVE GREETED THEM MORE ENTHUSIASTICALLY IF THEY REALLY **HAD** BEEN ROYALTY...

THE PEOPLE OF TICUARDA ARE **PROUD** THAT YOU HAVE HONOURED US BY GIVING OUR THREE FOOTBALL TEAMS THE CHANCE OF PLAYING AGAINST YOU, *THE GREATEST SOCCER SIDE IN THE WORLD!* IN RETURN, ILLUSTRIOUS SENORS, I OFFER YOU THE FREEDOM OF OUR LITTLE COUNTRY!

SKIPPER ROD ROPER GRINNED AT HIS BIG FRIEND STANDING BESIDE HIM...

...ON BEHALF OF ALL TICUARDA I SAY... WELCOME, *KINGS OF THE FOOTBALL FIELD!*

ADMIT YOU WERE WRONG, JIM! WE'RE IN FOR THE TIME OF OUR LIVES HERE!

BUT JIM BLACKER'S STUBBORN SCOWL ONLY DEEPENED...

HUMPH! I STILL SAY THERE'S SOMETHING FISHY ABOUT THAT *PANCHEZ* CHARACTER, ROD!

BUT, JIM, HE'S THE PRESIDENT'S CHIEF MINISTER! THIS WHOLE SCHEME WAS HIS **IDEA**! HE, OF ALL PEOPLE, WILL TRY TO MAKE THIS A SUCCESS!

AS THEY WERE DRIVEN THROUGH THE STREETS OF THE CAPITAL...

ANOTHER THING, ROD! LOOK AT THE PEOPLE! I'VE NEVER SEEN SUCH AN UNHAPPY LOOKING BUNCH!

YOU'RE WORSE THAN *'GLOOMY'* DAY, JIM! ANYWAY, TICUARDA IS SUPPOSED TO BE *FOOTBALL MAD!* SO THEY'LL CHEER UP WHEN WE PLAY OUR FIRST GAME TOMORROW!

THE STADIUM NEAR THE PRESIDENT'S PALACE WAS PACKED WITH SPECTATORS AS ROYAL'S RANGERS TOOK THE FIELD, BUT...

NOT A SINGLE SOUND, ROD! I THOUGHT YOU SAID THEY'D CHEER UP!

THEY'RE JUST SAVING THE CHEERS FOR THEIR OWN TEAM, JIM!

IN THE TOP ROOM OF A HIGH BUILDING, SENOR PANCHEZ RUBBED GLEEFUL HANDS AS THE BANDIT CARS SPED SAFELY FROM THE CITY...

PERFECT! NO-ONE WILL CATCH THEM NOW! YOU MUST DO *JUST AS GOOD A JOB* WITH YOUR *RIFLE!*

ALWAYS I *HIT* WHAT I *AIM* AT, SENOR MINISTER! *JUST SHOW ME THE TARGET!*

THERE IS YOUR TARGET, AMIGO! *ONE OF ROYAL'S RANGERS!*

WITH THIS TELESCOPIC SIGHT, IT WILL BE *EASY*, MINISTER! *WHICH ONE SHALL I SHOOT?*

THE BIG ONE! THE ONE WHO WAITS TO ATTACK OUR PLAYER! HE WILL DO NICELY! BUT DO NOT MISS!

I HAVE NOT DONE SO YET, SENOR MINISTER! I AM MOVING MY SIGHTS ON TO HIM NOW!

A SPLIT-SECOND LATER...

HUHH? DARN IT... HE'S *FAST!*

HE'S GOIN' TA DRIBBLE ROOND HIM! OR, HOOTS, HE *THINKS* HE IS!

AND AS FIERY LITTLE DIRK McKEE SPED BETWEEN THEM...

NO, YE DON'T... AAAAGH!

DIRK! HE - HE'S BEEN SHOT!

THE BULLET INTENDED FOR JIM BLACKER HAD HIT THE PEPPERY SCOT IN THE SHOULDER...

ACH! I- I'VE BEEN *BOOED* AT BEFORE BY THE CROWD... BUT NEVER *SHOT* AT!

I *KNEW* IT! I KNEW SOMETHING LIKE THIS WOULD HAPPEN! FOR PETE'S SAKE, *HURRY* WITH THAT STRETCHER!

BIG JIM'S FURIOUS GLARE SWEPT FROM THE PACKED STANDS TO ROD ROPER...

ROD, YOU'RE *SKIPPER!* LET'S *TURN THIS IN* RIGHT NOW BEFORE THINGS GET *WORSE!* AND THEY *WILL* IF WE *STAY* HERE!

MAYBE YOU ARE RIGHT, JIM! I'LL GO AND SEE BEN...

BUT THEN...

SO! THE FAMOUS RANGERS ARE *AFRAID!*

JUST A *STRAY* BULLET! IN TICUARDA THIS HAPPENS ALL THE TIME! IT IS... HOW YOU SAY:... *NORMAL!*

53

TWO DETERMINED ATTACKS PUT CAXFORD AHEAD EVEN FURTHER IN THE SECOND-HALF...

POW! A REAL TINY TIM TELFORD SPECIAL! HOW D'YA LIKE THAT, TICUARDA?

IT'S THERE! TWO UP!

AND WHEN THE FINAL WHISTLE BLEW, THE RANGERS HAD SCORED A GREAT FOUR-ONE VICTORY...

S'POSE WE DIDN'T DO TOO BAD! BUT POOR DIRK, HE GOT THE WORST OF IT!

CHEER UP, JIM! WE'LL GO AND SEE HIM AFTER WE'VE CHANGED!

BUT AS THE DOCTOR CLOSED THE DOOR ON THE SLEEPING SCOT...

QUICKLY! WE MUST DO OUR WORK BEFORE THEY COME BACK!

BUT AT THAT MOMENT, IN THE CITY HOSPITAL...

THOSE PILLS HAVE PUT HIM TO SLEEP ALREADY!

HE WILL FEEL MUCH BETTER WHEN HE AWAKES! AND WITH SUCH A SLIGHT WOUND THERE IS NO DANGER!

WELL, I HATE THEIR PERISHIN' CHIEF MINISTER...PANCHEZ! I KNOW THERE'S SOMETHING PHONEY ABOUT HIM!

JIM, ONCE YOU GET AN IDEA IN YOUR HEAD YOU NEVER LOSE IT, DO YOU? POOR OLD PANCHEZ! I BET HE'D BE UPSET IF HE COULD HEAR YOU!

MEANWHILE, BACK AT THE STADIUM...

A GOOD RESULT, JIM, CONSIDERING WE WERE PLAYING WITHOUT OUR STAR WINGER. YOU'D THINK THE FANS WOULD GIVE US JUST A FEW CHEERS!

I GET THE FEELING THEY HATE US, ROD! NOT THAT WE'VE DONE ANYTHING TO THEM!

BIG JIM BLACKER AND RANGERS' SKIPPER ROD ROPER HURRIED TO THE HOSPITAL TO WHICH DIRK McKEE HAD BEEN TAKEN ... AND THERE THEY SAW ...

ROD! THOSE TWO HAVE JUST CLIMBED DOWN FROM THAT WALL! WHAT'VE THEY BEEN UP TO?

THAT SUSPICIOUS MIND OF YOURS AGAIN, JIM! COME ON! IT'S NONE OF OUR BUSINESS!

THEY FOUND THEIR HIGHLAND-BORN WINGER BANDAGED BUT WELL ...

I FEEL FINE NOW! BUT ... HEY, WHAT'S BIG JIM LOOKING FOR?

AW, YOU KNOW JIM, DIRK! HE SAW A COUPLE OF FELLERS OUTSIDE DOWN THERE ... AND STRAIGHT AWAY HE'S SUSPECTING SOMETHING IS WRONG!

GO AHEAD AND GRIN! BUT I'VE BEEN RIGHT SO FAR! THAT WASN'T EXACTLY A MOSQUITO THAT BIT YOU!

OCH, WEEL, IT DOESNA HURT NOW! ALL AH FEEL BAD ABOUT IS I CANNA PLAY IN THE SECOND MATCH THE DAY AFTER TOMORROW! BUT AH'LL COME AND WATCH YE!

AT THAT MOMENT IT WAS THE PRESIDENT OF TICUARDA WHO WAS UPSET ...

AN INGLISI FOOTBALLER SHOT! THE STATE JEWELS STOLEN! YOU'RE SUPPOSED TO STOP SUCH OUTRAGES, PANCHEZ!

IT WILL NOT HAPPEN AGAIN, SENOR PRESIDENT!

ANOTHER THING ... WHY WASN'T I TOLD BEFORE THIS? I COULD HAVE ORDERED THE ARMY TO PURSUE THEM!

BUT, PRESIDENTO, YOU SAID YOURSELF YOU DID NOT WISH ANYTHING TO SPOIL YOUR ENJOYMENT OF THE MATCH!

IN THE CHANGING-ROOM, JUST BEFORE THE MATCH STARTED ...

GOOD LUCK TO YE, LADDIES!

WE'LL MISS YOU OUT THERE, DIRK! BUT WE BEAT THEIR FIRST TEAM AND WE'LL DO IT TO THIS LOT. YOU SHOULD BE FIT FOR THE THIRD MATCH!

AH HOPE IT'LL BE BETTER THEN, ROD! THEY'RE GOING TO CHANGE THE DRESSING SOME TIME TODAY! OUR FRIEND PANCHEZ HAS BROUGHT IN HIS OWN DOCTOR TO DO IT FOR ME!

PANCHEZ? I DON'T LIKE THAT! WHY DIDN'T HE LET THE ORDINARY DOCTORS DO IT?

OH, STREWTH! HERE WE GO AGAIN!

THERE'S YOUR FRIEND SENOR PANCHEZ UP THERE, JIM! TALKING TO DIRK! YOU DON'T SUPPOSE HE'S PLANTING A TIME BOMB UNDER HIM, DO YOU?

THAT'S RIGHT—LAUGH! BUT I TELL YOU I'LL BE PROVED RIGHT BEFORE THE DAY IS OUT! YOU'LL SEE!

CONTINUED ON PAGE 118

AROUND THE WORLD WITH DUNDEE

At the famous Aztec Stadium, Mexico, skipper Doug Smith met the Peruvian World Cup referee, Arturo Yamasaki.

No doubt you have all heard of the Harlem Globetrotters. The name explains itself as the famous American basketball side which tours the world.

Now meet Scotland's Soccer Globetrotters and, strangely enough, they are not involved with either of Glasgow's big two clubs, Rangers and Celtic.

When it comes to covering the globe, Dundee United are in a league of their own.

The story really begins some ten years ago with United only just established in the Scottish First Division. A short visit was arranged to Iceland during the close season and that started an incredible series of safaris for the club.

Since then they have journeyed all over the world, either as Cup competitors or simply football missionaries. From Mexico to Korea; Greece to Turkey; South Africa to the USA . . . **Dundee United are the travelling specialists.**

Perhaps their most sensational safari was the one which coincided with the 1970 World Cup in Mexico. Before the tournament started the Scots were invited to "warm-up"

UNITED!

Look, no grass! United played on a synthetic carpet at Oregon. Their opponents? West Ham!

Left: Action from United's game with a Mexico City XI.
Above: The lads outside the Mexican Football H.Q.

the Mexican fans in friendly games . . . but this was not as straightforward as it seemed.

The trip involved a journey from Scotland to Holland to Canada to America and then Mexico. From there they moved on to Greece via America, Canada and Europe. In total only 10 days were involved and a round trip of 25,000 miles.

Obviously the Scots were not upset by this as the following year they tackled another gigantic journey, this time to Seoul, the capital of Korea.

In between times they have been involved in trips all over America and Europe, and it's little wonder players joining this club must have up-to-date passports at all times.

SUPER SKIPPER

OVER this remarkable ten-year story, only one player has taken part in **every** trip . . . veteran skipper, Doug Smith.

He has led the side on to famous parks all over the world . . . the Camp Nou Stadium in Barcelona; the Olympic Stadium in Mexico City; the Municipal Stadium, Seoul; the Comunale, Turin, and dozens more.

But perhaps the one Doug will always remember is the smallest one of them all. A tiny park in the Rumanian town of Petrosani which is situated in the state of Transylvania, legendary 'haunting' ground of Count Dracula and 'friends'.

The trip was rated the worst ever undertaken by a United party and almost ended with disaster in a bus crash high in the Rumanian mountains. But no-one was hurt.

Now, with the space age rapidly approaching, who knows, Dundee United could be the first team to travel to the planets!

THE greatest player in the world was once considered to be the Brazilian bombshell, Pele, but now it's dazzling Dutchman Johann Cruyff, star of Ajax before his £922,000 transfer to Barcelona. A master of all the soccer arts, captain of Holland, his magic captivated the crowds at the 1974 World Cup Finals in Munich.

Brilliant ball-player with fantastic speed and scorer of amazing goals, Johann is the only man to win a hat-trick of European Footballer of the Year awards (1971-73-74). He was the superstar of Ajax in their three successive European Cup triumphs (1971-72-73) and the World Club Championship in 1972. Then came the 1974 World Cup Finals and if ever a man deserved a winner's medal it was Johann Cruyff, but he was robbed of the honour by the victorious West Germans.

JOHANN CRUYFF-SUPERSTAR

THE GOAL KINGS

There's nothing to delight the fans like a goal, so here are some of the men who hit the net regularly — six of the best!

DAVID JOHNSON
Ipswich Town

THE GOAL KINGS

'DIXIE' DEANS
Celtic

THE GOAL KINGS

BILLY JENNINGS
West Ham United

THE GOAL KINGS

FRANK WORTHINGTON
Leicester City

THE GOAL KINGS

DUNCAN McKENZIE
Leeds United

THE GOAL KINGS

PAUL FLETCHER
Burnley

BILLY'S BOOTS

YOUNG BILLY DANE WAS USELESS AT FOOTBALL UNTIL HE FOUND A PAIR OF FOOTBALL BOOTS THAT HAD ONCE BELONGED TO OLD-TIME SOCCER STAR, "DEAD-SHOT" KEEN, AND IN SOME STRANGE WAY THE BOOTS ENABLED HIM TO PLAY IN DEAD-SHOT'S STYLE. BILLY WAS IN GROUNDWOOD SCHOOL'S FIRST ELEVEN AND, AFTER LESSONS HAD FINISHED ONE AFTERNOON, HIS PALS WERE EAGER FOR A KICK-ABOUT...

LET'S HAVE A GAME OF FOOTBALL OVER THE REC!

GREAT! IT'LL BE GOOD PRACTICE FOR OUR CUP FINAL AGAINST CLEVELY SCHOOL IN A FORTNIGHT'S TIME!

YOU COMING ALONG WITH US, BILLY?

SORRY, BUT I WANT TO GET HOME EARLY! I'M GOING TO HAVE A BASH AT A FOOTBALL COMPETITION IN A MAGAZINE AND I MUST GET THE ENTRY OFF THIS EVENING!

WHEN BILLY ARRIVED HOME...

YOU'RE EARLY, BILLY! TEA WON'T BE READY FOR AT LEAST AN HOUR!

THAT'S OKAY, GRAN! I'VE GOT SOMETHING VERY IMPORTANT TO DO!

IN HIS ROOM...

RIGHT, JUST FOUR MORE QUESTIONS TO GO AND I'LL BE FINISHED!

AND VERY SHORTLY...

THERE – ALL THROUGH! I ONLY HOPE THAT I'VE MANAGED TO GET THE ANSWERS CORRECT!

BILLY WAS MET BY THE CLUB'S MANAGER, EX-INTERNATIONAL STAR. BILL REYNOLDS.

HELLO, BILLY! I'M GOING TO SHOW YOU AROUND THE PLACE, SO IF THERE'S ANYTHING YOU WANT TO KNOW, DON'T BE AFRAID TO ASK!

THANK YOU, SIR!

IT WAS A TREMENDOUS DAY FOR BILLY...

THIS IS THE HOME TEAM'S DRESSING-ROOM!

IT'S A BIT BETTER THAN THE ONE WE USE AT MY SCHOOL!

YOU'RE JUST IN TIME TO SEE THE FIRST TEAM IN A FIVE-A-SIDE GAME!

THAT'S ENGLAND STAR MARTIN PAYNE ON THE BALL! HE'S A GREAT PLAYER!

AND BILLY EVEN GOT A KICK OF THE BALL ON HIGHDOWN'S FAMOUS PITCH...

GREAT SHOT, BILLY!

IT WASN'T BAD CONSIDERING I HAVEN'T GOT DEAD-SHOT'S BOOTS ON!

THE VISIT CONCLUDED WITH A LOOK AT THE CLUB'S IMPRESSIVE TROPHY ROOM...

TAKE AS MUCH TIME AS YOU LIKE IN HERE, BILLY!

IT'S FANTASTIC! I NEVER REALISED THAT ROVERS HAD WON SO MUCH DURING THEIR HISTORY!

HEY, THIS IS A PICTURE OF THE HIGHDOWN TEAM AFTER THEY'D WON THE CUP IN THE THIRTIES. BUT MY HERO DEAD-SHOT KEEN IS *MISSING* FROM IT!

I'M SURE HE PLAYED IN THAT FINAL, SO WHY ISN'T HE IN THE PHOTOGRAPH?

I'VE NO IDEA, BILLY! BUT OUR HEAD GROUNDSMAN, TED WILLIAMS, HAS BEEN WITH THE CLUB FOR WELL OVER FORTY YEARS, PERHAPS HE'LL REMEMBER! WHY DON'T YOU HAVE A WORD WITH HIM?

THE VETERAN GROUNDSMAN WAS MARKING OUT THE PITCH...

EXCUSE ME, SIR, BUT DO YOU KNOW IF ANYTHING HAPPENED TO DEAD-SHOT KEEN THE DAY THE CLUB WON THE CUP IN THE THIRTIES?

AYE, I DO, LAD! I REMEMBER IT VERY WELL!

A REAL HERO DEAD-SHOT WAS THAT SUNNY AFTERNOON! HIGHDOWN WERE PLAYING SEADON RANGERS AND THE SCORE WAS TWO GOALS EACH WITH ONLY A FEW MINUTES LEFT TO PLAY!

"... THEN DEAD-SHOT GOT POSSESSION AND SENT A LONG PASS TO A TEAM-MATE..."

"... AND HE WENT HARING INTO THE PENALTY AREA AS THE BALL WAS CHIPPED BEAUTIFULLY INTO HIS PATH..."

"...DEAD-SHOT SCORED A WONDERFUL GOAL! BUT THE SPEED OF HIS RUN WAS SO GREAT HE COULDN'T STOP..."

"...AND HE CRASHED INTO THE POST, INJURING HIMSELF BADLY..."

AYE, HIGHDOWN WON THE CUP THAT DAY, BUT POOR DEAD-SHOT WAS BEING STRETCHERED OFF WHEN THE REST OF THE PLAYERS WENT UP FOR THE TROPHY!

G-GOSH!

ON THE WAY HOME, BILLY WAS WORRIED BY THE GROUNDSMAN'S STORY...

I'M PLAYING IN A CUP FINAL FOR MY SCHOOL TOMORROW... AND WHAT ONCE HAPPENED TO DEAD-SHOT USUALLY HAPPENS TO ME AS WELL WHEN I'M WEARING THE BOOTS! CRIKEY, I DON'T WANT TO BE INJURED!

IN GROUNDWOOD SCHOOL'S DRESSING-ROOM ON THE DAY OF THE FINAL...

I'VE GOT TO TRY AND PUT DEAD-SHOT KEEN OUT OF MY MIND... BUT IT WON'T BE EASY!

GROUNDWOOD KICKED-OFF TO A ROAR FROM THE FANS...

GROUNDWOOD!

CLEVELY!

GROUNDWOOD!

CLEVELY!

AND ALMOST AT ONCE, BILLY FOUND HIMSELF WITH A GREAT CHANCE...

HIT IT FIRST TIME, BILLY!

DANE CAN'T MISS!

BUT...

YAAH! WHAT A ROTTEN SHOT!

MY KID SISTER COULD HAVE SCORED FROM THERE!

I MUST BE STILL WORRIED ABOUT THE DEAD-SHOT KEEN INCIDENT!

BILLY CONTINUED TO PLAY BADLY, BUT BOTH TEAMS WERE FINDING DIFFICULTY IN SCORING. THEN, MIDWAY THROUGH THE SECOND-HALF, WITH THE GAME LOCKED IN A GOALLESS DRAW...

I RECKON WE'RE IN FOR SOME RAIN! THOSE HEAVY BLACK CLOUDS HAVE BEEN BUILDING UP FOR THE PAST HALF AN HOUR!

BILLY WAS THE ONLY ONE PLEASED WHEN THE CLOUD-BURST HIT THE GROUND...

I REMEMBER THE OLD GROUNDSMAN SAYING THAT DEAD-SHOT'S FINAL WAS PLAYED ON A SUNNY DAY! WELL, IT'S CERTAINLY NOT SUNNY HERE, SO NOW I CAN FORGET ABOUT EVERYTHING ELSE AND HELP GROUNDWOOD TO WIN THIS MATCH!

THE RAIN HAD STOPPED WHEN BILLY GOT THE BALL IN THE MIDDLE OF THE PITCH AND SAW THAT HIS WINGER WAS CLEAR...

CRIKEY! THIS IS ALMOST THE SAME SITUATION THAT HAPPENED TO DEAD-SHOT!

THERE CAN ONLY BE SECONDS LEFT TO PLAY, AND I'VE GOT TO GET OUR FORWARD LINE ON THE ATTACK!

GREAT BALL! THE WINGER'S AWAY!

THEN, SUDDENLY...

HEY, THE BOOTS ARE MAKING ME SPRINT UP THE MIDDLE! I-I DON'T WANT TO — BUT I CAN'T STOP MYSELF!

THE WINGER CENTRED THE BALL...

THIS MUST BE GROUNDWOOD'S LAST CHANCE!

LOOK AT DANE — HE'S RUNNING LIKE MAD INTO THE PENALTY AREA!

IT WAS AN IDENTICAL GOAL TO THE ONE DEAD-SHOT KEEN HAD SCORED OVER FORTY YEARS BEFORE...

IT'S THERE!

WHAT A GOAL FROM BILLY!

BUT...

HE'S GOING TO CRASH INTO THE UPRIGHT!

HE CAN'T STOP!

I CAN'T BEAR TO WATCH!

THEN BILLY'S BOOT LANDED IN A PATCH OF SLIPPERY MUD...

AAAARGH!

AND, INCREDIBLY...

HE'S OKAY! HE'S GONE SLIDING PAST THE POST!

WELL DONE, BILLY!

IT WAS THE ONLY GOAL OF THE GAME... AND BILLY WAS ABLE TO COLLECT HIS WINNER'S MEDAL...

THAT WAS A VERY BRAVE GOAL YOU SCORED, YOUNG MAN! YOUR TEAM-MATES MUST BE VERY PROUD OF YOU!

THANK YOU, SIR!

BILLY WAS THE HERO OF THE HOUR...

GROUNDWOOD!

GROUNDWOOD!

BUT FOR THE RAIN I WOULD HAVE BEEN INJURED! THIS IS ONE DAY WHEN I'M REALLY GLAD THAT THE BOOTS SLIPPED UP FOR ME!

THE END

SUPER REDS

Classy Mick Channon in the colours of Southampton.

Arfon Griffiths wears red for his club Wrexham and also his country, Wales. He's a midget marvel in midfield.

Emlyn Hughes, captain of Merseyside "Reds" and star of England. He joined Liverpool from Blackpool.

Tony Towers gained England Under-23 honours with Manchester City before donning the red and white shirt of Sunderland in March, 1974.

Derek Possee, Orient's tiny terror. A fearless striker, he played for Spurs, Millwall and Palace before joining O's.

Tony Field, Sheffield United's dashing left-wing goalgetter and former leading scorer for Southport and Blackburn Rovers.

Arthur Horsfield, popular hot-shot with Charlton, also wore red with Middlesbro' and Swindon before his transfer to London.

George Lyall, one of Nottingham Forest's star Scots, can play anywhere — and score goals, too.

John Mahoney (left), wears red for Wales and red and white for Stoke City. He's a great midfield-striker.

Alan Foggon, Middlesbrough forward (right), is proud to be a Red at Ayresome Park.

Brian Kidd (above), Arsenal's star from Manchester United — also red!

Willie Morgan, captain of Manchester United and Scotland World Cup star, was with Burnley before joining United.

Drew Jarvie, Scottish capped strike-leader at Aberdeen, was formerly with Airdrie — who wear red and white.

SUB.

HE'S ALWAYS ON THE SIDELINES!

SATURDAY AFTERNOON — AND DUGGIE DRIBBLE, THE WANDERERS' SUBSTITUTE, WAS PASSING THE TIME WITH A CROSSWORD PUZZLE — TRYING TO HIT ON THE WORD — "SUET DUMPLING"...

ER — WHAT'S PLUMP, PALE AND SPINELESS — WITH THE INITIALS S.D.?

SUBSTITUTE DRIBBLE!

...AND, IF YOU WANNA BECOME SLIM AND RUGGED — WITH GUTS — GET SOME EXERCISE! TAG ALONG WITH BILL GRIM, OUR GOALIE, ON HIS NEXT FOUR-MILE SPRINT ROUND THE DOCKS!

(GULP!) Y-YES, MISTER MANAGER-SIR!

SO, THE FOLLOWING SATURDAY MORNING...

STOP! (GASP!) I CAN'T GO ON! (WHEEZE) — NOT USED TO IT! (PANT) M-MUST HAVE A BREATHER!

HUN! THAT'S AFTER A 20 YARD JOG-TROT JUST TO LIMBER UP!

OKAY! WE'LL REST!

DOCK REGULATIONS

SUDDENLY, WHILE RESTING, DUGGIE HAD A BRILLIANTLY DIABOLICAL IDEA TO RID HIS TEAM OF BILL GRIM — SO THAT HE WOULD BE ABLE TO SUB, AS GOALIE, DURING THE AFTERNOON MATCH...

SHANGHAI ROSE

HEH, HEH! I'LL GET HIM "SHANGHAIED"!

SHANGHAI

OFFICE

ORIENT EXPORT Cº Lº

AND SO...

COR! GUESS WHAT'S GONNA BE EXPORTED IN THIS!

TAKE A LOOK!

BILL DID TAKE A LOOK, AND...

YOU, PAL!

HUP!

ZIP

ERK!

SHANGHAI

HEH, HEH! *GOODBYE, GRIM!* NO ONE'LL HEAR YOUR YELLS ABOVE THE DOCKSIDE CLATTER! SAVE YOUR VOICE FOR LEARNING *CHINESE!*

BANG BANG

SHANGHAI

M-M-M-M! LEMME OUT!

BUT, AFTER DUGGIE HAD SKEDADDLED . . .

WHAT FOOL *LABELLED* THIS CRATE *"SHANGHAI"?* IT'S ONLY JUST ARRIVED *FROM* CHINA! CHEAP GYM EQUIPMENT MADE IN HONG KONG FOR A *CRUMMY FOOTBALL TEAM!* I'LL GET IT RE-LABELLED AND DELIVERED BY *ROAD!*

SHANGHAI

THE BOX WAS RE-LABELLED AND LOADED ON TO A LORRY . . .

WHERE TO, ALF?

WANDERERS' FOOTBALL GROUND!

MMM

THAT AFTERNOON, IN BIGGLESWICK WANDERERS' DRESSING-ROOM . . .

DRIBBLE! GRIM HASN'T TURNED UP-AND KICK-OFF'S IN FIFTEEN MINUTES! UNPACK THAT NEW GYM EQUIPMENT THAT'S JUST ARRIVED, AND I'LL LET YOU SUB FOR HIM!

OH, BOY!

HEE-HEE! *SUCCESS!*

BLOATED WITH TRIUMPH, DUGGIE WADDLED EXCITEDLY TO THE GYM . . .

WELL, WELL! *WHADDYA-KNOW!* IT'S THE SAME KIND-A CRATE OL' BILL GRIM'S BOUND FOR *SHANGHAI* IN!

-HA-HA-HA!-

SNARL!

WANDERERS' FOOTBALL STADIUM

GYM

AWLK! YOU'VE BEEN DEPORTED ALREADY!

GRR-R! WHAT I'M GONNA DO TO *YOU NOW*, DRIBBLE, IS GONNA MAKE WHAT *YOU* TRIED TO DO TO ME *LOOK SILLY!*

WANDERERS' FOOTBALL STADIUM KESWICK

-SNARL! GNASH! GRIND!

GYM

A FEW MINUTES LATER, AFTER BILL GRIM HAD *DONE IT*— AND GONE! . . .

IT'S OKAY, DRIBBLE! GRIM'S *TURNED UP!* YOU CAN CARRY ON WITH YOUR *CROSSWORD PUZZLE,* NOW!

GYM

SIGH OF RELIEF

RAP-RAP

HUH! YOU FINISH IT! *I'M* WORKING ON A *CHINESE PUZZLE,* MATE!

JERK

TUG

GRUNT

79

HALF-TIME HOWLERS

Hot-Shot Hamish

HAMISH BALFOUR WAS A GIANT HEBRIDEAN ISLANDER WHO WAS BROUGHT TO THE MAINLAND TO PLAY FOR SCOTTISH SECOND DIVISION CLUB, PRINCES PARK. HAMISH HAD A TREMENDOUS HOT-SHOT AND HE HELPED PRINCES TO WIN THE SCOTTISH CUP. THEN ONE CHRISTMAS TIME...

WE'RE LEAVING YE IN CHARGE, HAMISH! YE'VE NOTHING T'DO BUT GET THE LADS TO STICK UP POSTERS ADVERTISING OUR NEW YEAR CHARITY GAME. MR. McWHACKER AND I WILL BE BACK ON THE DAY O' THE MATCH...

DINNA WORRY, MR. McBRAIN...I'LL SEE THINGS RUN SMOOTH WHILE YE'RE AWAY!

AND MAKE SURE THE LADS GET SOME TRAINING IN...

THE POSTERS FOR THE CHARITY MATCH FOR CHILDREN WERE ALREADY PRINTED...

STICK 'EM UP ALL OVER THE TOON, LADS...WE WANT A *BIG* CROWD!

OCH, WE ALWAYS GET A BIG CROWD ON NEW YEAR'S DAY, MON!

IT'S A GOOD CAUSE WE'LL BE PLAYING FER, HAMISH! I LIKE CHILDREN!

SO DO I, MON... I WAS ONE M'SEL' ONCE, YE KEN!

PRINCES PARK F.C. v AFRICAN ARROWS

MATCH JANUARY 1st

ALL PROCEEDS

CHILDRENS' FUND

OCH, YE DINNA KEN YER OWN STRENGTH, HAMISH!

I HARDLY GAVE IT A TAP, MON! THIS STAND IS VERY OLD...IT MUST BE NEARLY FALLING T'BITS!

YE'LL NO' DO MUCH USE COVERING THE HOLE WI' BROWN PAPER, HAMISH! THE RAIN'LL SOON GET IN THERE!

I'LL FIX IT PROPERLY LATER ON! WHAT WE HA' TO DO THE NOO, IS SOME TRAINING! I PROMISED OUR MANAGER THAT WE'D ALL KEEP FIT!

AND SO, THE PRINCES PARK PLAYERS GOT DOWN TO A TRAINING SESSION...

SNAP TO IT, LADS... MOVE QUICKLY! THERE'S NO' MUCH TO LEAP-FROGGIN' O'ER WEE WALLIE WALLACE!

AW COME ON, WALLIE, YE'RE NO' TRYING!

JUMPING O'ER YE IS LIKE CLIMBING MOUNT EVEREST! IT'S NO' FAIR!

OHHHH! THERE MAY BE NOTHING TO IT FER YE, HAMISH, BUT YE'RE DRIVING ME INTO THE GROUND!

THEY SAY THIS AFRICAN TEAM IS RED-HOT, HAMISH! WE'LL HA' A JOB T'BEAT 'EM!

PRINCES PARK ARE A RED-HOT TEAM, TOO, MON! BY THE TIME I'VE FINISHED WI' YE... YE'LL BE FITTER THAN MR. McWHACKER HAS EVER SEEN YE!

I'LL PUMP SOME LONG CROSSFIELD PASSES TO YE, LADS... I WANT YE TO BANG 'EM BACK AGAIN...

HE'S NO' GOING T'MAKE US TRAIN ALL DAY LONG, IS HE? I WANT MA DINNER!

IT'S A' RIGHT FER HAMISH... HE NEVER SEEMS TO GET TIRED!

HAMISH LET FLY...

TRAP THE BA'... AND BANG IT BACK!

OCH, I'M NO' GETTING IN THE WAY O' THAT!

YE'RE SUPPOSED T'BE PASSING THE BALL, HAMISH... NOT TRYING OUT YER HOT-SHOT!

YE KICKED EVERY BALL INTO THE STAND, HAMISH...SO *YE* CAN GET 'EM BACK!

AYE! WE'VE HAD ENO' RUNNING AROUND FER TODAY!

OKAY... I'LL GO!

OCH, AWA'! WHAT'S HAPPENED HERE?

THE FOOTBALLS WENT CLEAN THROUGH THE WOODWORK! OCH, THE OLD STAND'S FALLING T'BITS! THE WOODWORK'S ROTTEN! *IT'S NO' SAFE!*

WHAT HA' YE GOT THERE, HAMISH?

THE STAND'S FALLING TO PIECES, LADS! THIS MORNING I BANGED A HAMMER THROUGH THE SIDE...AND NOW THE FOOTBALLS HA' GONE CLEAN THROUGH THE WOODWORK! THE PLACE IS *DANGEROUS!*

IF WE CANNA USE THAT STAND...WE WON'T GET HALF AS MANY PEOPLE IN FER THE CHARITY MATCH!

COULD WE NO' PULL THE STAND DOON... AND RE-BUILD IT?

WE'D NEVER GET IT DONE IN TIME! IT'D TAKE A COUPLE O' DAYS JUST TO PULL IT DOON, LET ALONE RE-BUILD IT!

OCH, IT'LL NO' TAKE TWO DAYS T'PULL IT DOON ...IT'LL TAKE TWO *MINUTES!* GIMME A SLEDGE-HAMMER AND I'LL SHOW YE!

THE BIG HEBRIDEAN WENT TO WORK...LIKE A HURRICANE!

CRRR-OOOUNNCH!

A B C D E F G H I J

OCH, HE'S A ONE-MON EARTHQUAKE!

K L M N O

WELL, IT'S DOON, HAMISH...BUT WHO'S GONNA PUT IT UP AGAIN?

WE'LL GET THE BUILDERS IN, OF COURSE!

IT'LL COST A FORTUNE TO REBUILD!

AYE! IT'LL COST MORE THAN WE TAKE AT THE GATE FER A YEAR!

THEN WE'LL GET THE FAN CLUB T'HELP!

I DINNA KEN WHY YE WANT THE LOUD-SPEAKERS TO BE TURNED AROUND, HAMISH! WHAT'S THE IDEA?

I WANT T'TALK TO THE PRINCES PARK FANS, MON... I CANNA WRITE LETTERS TO 'EM... IT'D TAKE TOO LONG! I'LL TALK TO 'EM ALL TOGETHER...

HAMISH WENT UP TO THE CLUB'S COMMENTARY BOX...

THIS IS HOT-SHOT HAMISH...CALLING A' PRINCES PARK FANS! CAN YE HEAR ME? I'VE A JOB FER YE T'DO...

IN THE TOWN...

...WE WANT VOLUNTEERS TO COME ALONG AN' HELP RE-BUILD THE STAND BEFORE THE CHARITY MATCH. BRING YER OWN WOOD AND HAMMERS AND EVERYTHING...IT'S HAMISH BALFOUR ASKING YE...

OCH, WE'LL HA' TO HELP HAMISH...

I'LL GO...

ME, TOO...

THE BIG MON NEEDS A HAND!

PRINCES PARK NEEDS US!

RECONSTRUCTION WORK BEGAN AT ONCE AS THE FANS RALLIED ROUND...

THAT'S THE IDEA, LADS...SOON AS THE OLD WOOD'S OUT...THE NEW STUFF GOES IN!

THEY WORKED ALL DAY LONG...

LEFT A BIT, HAMISH...

UP A BIT, HAMISH, LAD!

HAMISH IS DOING THE WORK O' TEN MEN!

AND ALL NIGHT, TOO...

SUPPER'S READY... COME ON, EVERYONE!

IT'S GOING T'BE FINISHED BY NEW YEAR'S DAY!

AYE, AN' IT'S ALL DUE TO HAMISH BALFOUR ...HE'S WORKED HIS FINGERS TO THE BONE!

AND THE STAND WAS COMPLETED! BUT, ON NEW YEAR'S EVE...

SNOW! OCH, THE PITCH WILL NO' BE FIT T'PLAY IF THIS KEEPS UP! I'LL HA' TO TROT OOT THERE AND INSPECT IT!

AT DAWN'S FIRST LIGHT...

I DINNA LIKE THE LOOK O' IT, HAMISH! WE'LL NO' BE PLAYING OOT HERE T'DAY!

MAYBE IT'S NO' AS BAD AS IT LOOKS...!

THE GENTLE GIANT TRIED A PRACTISE DRIBBLE...

YON BALL'S GETTING *BIGGER* AN' *BIGGER*!

TRY A WEE KICK, HAMISH!

ARRRGHHH! M'TOE!

IF YE CANNA KICK THE BALL, HAMISH... *NO-ONE* CAN! WE'LL HA' TO CANCEL THE MATCH AFTER ALL! IT'S A TERRIBLE SHAME!

WE'VE GOT A NEW STAND ...AND NO PITCH T'PLAY ON! IF WE DINNA PLAY THE NEW YEAR CHARITY GAME...WE'LL BE LETTING DOON ALL OUR FANS!

BUT WHAT CAN WE DO?

I'VE GOT AN IDEA! *FLAME-THROWERS!* YE GET SOME WATER-PUMPS, WALLIE...AND CALL THE TEAM IN T'HELP!

WATER-PUMPS... *FLAME-THROWERS?* OCH, THE BIG FELLER'S GONE COMPLETELY BARMY!

BUT HAMISH'S IDEA PROVED SUCCESSFUL...

THIS IS THE BEST SNOW-MELTER IN THE BUSINESS, LADS! GET YON WATER-PUMP READY!

IT MAY WORK... I CAN SEE THE GRASS!

YE'RE RIGHT, MON ...*WE'RE GOING* T'PLAY AFTER ALL...!

FOLLOWED BY WHAT EVERYONE HAD BEEN WAITING FOR...

THE HOT-SHOT!

AT THE END, IT WAS A TWO-NIL VICTORY FOR PRINCES PARK...

GREAT GAME, MAN!

THAT HAMISH HITS A BALL LIKE HE *HATED* IT!

WELL PLAYED, LADDIE!

PRINCES PARK PLAYERS WISH A HAPPY NEW YEAR TO THE BEST FANS IN FOOTBA'!

HAPPY NEW YEAR T'PRINCES PARK! THE BEST TEAM IN SCOTLAND!

HURRRAHHH!

MANAGER MR. McWHACKER WAS WAITING AT THE TUNNEL...

SORRY I COULDNA GET HERE SOONER, LADS! DID YE HA' ANY TROUBLE WHILE I WAS AWA', HAMISH? DID EVERYTHING RUN SMOOTHLY?

TROUBLE? OH, NO, MR. McWHACKER!

I CANNA THINK O' ANYTHING THAT WENT WRONG, SIRRR! IT'S NO TROUBLE AT ALL LOOKING AFTER A FOOTBA' CLUB — NO TROUBLE AT ALL...!

The END

EMLYN HUGHES
Liverpool

COLIN TODD
Derby

MICK CHANNON
Southampton

PETER SHILTON
Stoke

89

Bobby

" **L**OST something, Dad?"

The question came from Bobby Booth, player-manager and skipper of Everpool City, the club nicknamed **The Blues.**

His father was roaming the room, opening drawers, looking under cushions.

" My new ratchet screwdriver. It's a good one. Expensive. I want to fix that loose mirror in the bathroom," he said.

" It's all right," Bobby's mother called from the kitchen. " Joey's got your screwdriver. He and Peggy Reed from next door are out in the garage, making a banner."

" **What?**" exclaimed his father. " If he's damaged it, I'll . . . "

" I'm surprised at you, Robert," smiled Bobby's mother as she came into the room. " You're always complaining about young people behaving like hooligans. Now that he's interested in doing something public spirited and useful, like working for this **Conservation Society,** you ought to be encouraging him."

" I *have* encouraged him," retorted Bobby's father. " I gave him a fiver as a donation to the society so that I could be enrolled as a vice-president."

" That's nice," smiled Mrs Booth. " We're both vice-presidents. I gave him five pounds, too."

At that moment Joey came in, grinning, with Peggy. They were carrying a banner wrapped round two poles.

" How about you supporting us, too, Bobby?" he demanded. " It's a very serious matter, you know, making people understand about conservation. Otherwise we'll soon all end up buried under our own rubbish."

" Will a couple of quid do?" Bobby asked, taking out his wallet.

" Don't be mean! Mum and Dad gave us five each," said Joey scornfully.

" Looks to me as if you're making a good thing out of this," chuckled Bobby as he handed over a fiver. " You must be raking in a fortune."

" We're **not** making anything out of it!" protested Peggy indignantly. " We give all the donations t our organiser, Adrian Cowley, for campaign expense You should meet Adrian—he's smashing."

" Where did you meet this chap?" asked Bobb curiously.

" In the park, actually," Peggy replied. " H goes there a lot to feed the ducks. He's very fond c all kinds of animals and bird life."

" I've seen him," said Bobby's mother. " H always seems to have a lot of young people round him Very attractive."

" Dishy!" agreed Peggy dreamily, and Joey scowled

" There's something else I've got to tell you," h said. " I shan't be coming to the Merseaport match."

Bobby was staggered.

Merseaport were the Blues' great local rivals an their clashes were always among the biggest events o the season. He had never known his younge brother miss such a game before.

" We're going on a demo," explained Joey. " W haven't been told what it is yet, but Adrian says it' our great chance to make our cause known, an **everyone** must be on it."

When Joey and Peggy had gone Bobby turned to his father in amazement.

" Phew! This fellow Cowley must have a fantasti cally persuasive personality, if he can talk Joey and hi pals into missing the Merseaport match," he said " I wonder what they're up to?".

PROTEST

BOBBY was destined to find out when the Blues reached Merseaport.

It was a cold and damp afternoon. There had bee heavy rain during the morning, and there was th threat of more to come.

" The pitch is bound to be slow, and the ball will b heavy," Bobby warned his players in the dressing-room " Don't expect to be able to get away with any cleve stuff. Merseaport won't allow you the time for that."

When the players ran out, the welcoming cheer which greeted them changed abruptly to yells o astonishment.

of the Blues

Bobby turned round to learn the cause, and was amazed to see a crowd of banner-carrying teenagers parading round the touchline. The banners bore slogans such as **Save the Trees** and **Stop Vandalism.**

It didn't take Bobby long to spot Joey and Peggy in the procession.

He turned in amazement to the Merseaport skipper.

"What's all the fuss about?" he asked.

"It's the trees round the car park," the rival captain explained. "They're diseased and dangerous, and they've got to come down. But this new conservation society is protesting like mad."

The crowds on the terraces took sides. Some cheered, others jeered, and for a few minutes the stadium was in an uproar. Then the protesters, having made their point, settled down quietly outside the touchline, to allow the game to begin.

As Bobby had predicted, both sides found the muddy turf difficult and treacherous.

Everpool were the first to attack. Don Westlake sent a long ball through to Bobby, and the Blues' fans yelled with excitement which turned to dismay as Bobby failed to steady himself properly on the slippery ground, and shot wide.

The resulting goalkick gave the Merseaport striker the chance to break through and test Ted Anderson with a thunderbolt shot. Ted grabbed the greasy ball and hugged it to his chest as it spun wildly in his hands.

By half-time neither side had completely mastered the tricky conditions, and there was no score.

As the referee blew for the start of the second-half there was a yell from the demonstrators round the field, and they swarmed on to the playing area, waving their banners.

But now the spectators, who had taken the first demonstration in good spirit, were furious at the interference.

"**Chuck 'em off! Throw 'em out!**" they yelled.

Police came on to the pitch and there were wild scuffles. Bobby glimpsed Joey yelling defiance, and grabbed him.

"You **blithering** little idiot," he said furiously.

"**Get off the pitch!**"

"What **else** could we do?" protested Joey. "We tried to avoid trouble by asking the club management to give us a promise not to cut down the trees! We warned them there'd be another demonstration if they didn't keep their word and they ignored us!"

"Do you realise that Mum and Dad are here, watching this carry-on? How do you suppose *they* feel?" asked Bobby furiously.

"**Blame Merseaport, not me,**" retorted Joey.

STORM

AT that moment the rain that had been threatening all the afternoon suddenly began to come down in sheets.

The demonstrators were soaked through, and fled for cover.

With the pitch cleared, the game was resumed, but it was impossible for either side to play anything like real football.

Everybody, including the spectators, was pleased when it was over, with no goals scored. In the circumstances it was fair to both clubs that they should share the points.

After a shower and a change into dry clothes Bobby picked up his parents to drive them home.

The car park was awash, and strewn with leaves fallen from the surrounding trees.

Then, as Bobby drove away, he lost control of the car for a second or two as it went into a skid on the wet leaves, the steering wheel feeling absolutely useless in his hands.

"Wow, that **was** nasty!" said his father.

"Good job there was no-one near," agreed Bobby, slightly shaken. "No matter what Joey and his pals say, those trees certainly ought to come down."

Joey arrived home later, looking rather sheepish. He tried to avoid the rest of the family by slipping up to his room, but Bobby grabbed him.

"Personally, I couldn't care less if you want to make a fool of yourself," Bobby told him sternly. "But this conservation caper is upsetting Mum and Dad. You've got to pack it in."

"But I **can't**!" protested Joey. "I've promised my support and I'm not letting Adrian Cowley down by backing out now. It would be like leaving your mates in the lurch by running away from a fight!"

Early the following week Bobby was driving past the Merseaport stadium, and was astounded to hear the sound of power saws. Seeing the trees around the car park toppling, he pulled up to watch, and then noticed the Merseaport captain coming out of the stadium.

"What is Cowley's Conservation Society going to say about this?" asked Bobby with a grin. "Has the club decided to defy the protesters?"

"And have more matches disrupted? Not likely!" answered Bobby's rival. "Apparently Cowley came down and chatted-up our chairman saying that if you can't beat 'em, join 'em!"

"I don't quite follow," frowned Bobby.

"Simple. We gave a nice big donation to his society and then asked him to take another look at the trees. He did, and decided that we were right, that they were dangerous and should come down."

"In other words, you bought him off," said Bobby scornfully.

"It's all very well for you to take that attitude," retorted the other. "We owe it to our fans to avoid trouble. If it happened to the Blues you'd change **your** mind."

When Bobby got home he told Joey what he had learned.

"Adrian Cowley is a crook!" Bobby insisted. "He's just using you and the rest of the people in your society to force money out of honest people."

But Joey, like the others, had been so charmed by Cowley's personality, that he refused to believe his brother.

"He is **not** a crook! The society **must** have money to carry on its work," Joey protested furiously. "You make it sound terrible but Adrian puts it quite differently, and he can explain it all."

"I bet he can. He's a smooth-talking con-man," Bobby retorted grimly. "Anyway, now that Merseaport have bought him off, I wonder who he'll pick on next?"

Bobby didn't have to wait long to find out.

The following morning The Blues were holding a training session in preparation for an important home league game against Mandover.

Suddenly, there was wild commotion near the tunnel.

Bobby turned in the direction of the sound, and couldn't believe his eyes.

A herd of cows was wandering on to the pitch, driven by a smiling, pleasant-faced young man.

Bobby raced across to him.

"What do you think **you're** doing?" he demanded.

"Making a protest. I'm Adrian Cowley, of the Conservation Society. You've probably heard of me," he smiled.

"I certainly have," Bobby said grimly. "What are you protesting about this time?"

With a friendly smile Cowley unfolded an old map. "It's this public footpath, you see. Goes right across the pitch. Blues have no right to keep it closed. It was granted centuries ago, so that a farmer who had two fields, separated by what is now the stadium, could move his cattle from one field to the other," he explained.

"But there are no fields for miles now, so who wants to drive cattle across our pitch?" Bobby exploded.

"I do," answered Cowley blandly.

Vic Crosby, Blues' general manager, had come out on to the pitch, scowling.

"Of course, I realise that this could be a terrible inconvenience to you," Cowley continued, "especially if I felt I wanted to use the path just when you were in the middle of your match against Mandover, as I probably shall." He went on in apologetic tones: "I'm afraid I'll have to insist, unless, of course, you care to follow Merseaport's example, and join the society."

"And how much is the subscription?" demanded Bobby.

"Five hundred pounds," said Cowley with his polite smile.

Vic took a deep breath to control his anger.

"You're a scheming scoundrel," he said fiercely. "But there's nothing the club can do about you, so come up to my office and I'll give you a cheque."

"No, wait, Vic," protested Bobby. "We're not giving in *that* easily. There's still three days to the Mandover game—time to find some other way of dealing with this crook!"

Cowley turned with a shrug to drive his cows back to waiting cattle trucks.

"Take all the time you need," he said cheerily, "and when you discover that I'm right you'll probably find me in the park, feeding the ducks."

"Feeding the ducks!" echoed Bobby scornfully.

Vic was convinced that the club would have to surrender in the end, but his skipper insisted that they should put up a fight by engaging private enquiry agents to find out more about Adrian Cowley, who had been in Everpool only a few weeks and seemed to have no past.

STRANGE FINDINGS

BY Thursday evening, Bobby had some interesting news for Joey and Peggy.

"What do you two know about Aldous Cunningham, Ashley Cardew, and Austin Carruthers, to name but a few?" asked Bobby.

"Never heard of any of 'em," admitted Joey, mystified. "Who are they?"

"They're all names used by Adrian Cowley in other places, before he came here. He operates the same way every time . . . starts up a society, gets a lot of trusting teenagers to support him, collects big money from people to whom his society will be a nuisance and then disappears with the cash," Bobby told him.

"Then he **is** a crook, after all," groaned Joey in dismay. "Are you going to the police?"

"When someone starts up a society, collects donations, then pockets most of the funds, claiming they'd gone on his expenses, it is a long and hard

Bobby and his Everpool team-mates gasped in astonishment. Their own stadium had been invaded by an enormous herd of hungry cows.

business to prove a swindle," Bobby explained. "It certainly couldn't be done by Saturday. We've got to find some other way to clobber him."

He turned to Peggy.

"I've had an idea. He tried to twist us by producing some ancient local law that no-one knew anything about. Perhaps we could turn the tables. You work at the town hall, Peggy—could you get permission to search the Everpool archives?"

"I'm sure I could," smiled Peggy. "Be there in the morning."

Bobby spent a dusty Friday in the basement of the town hall, searching through shelves of yellowing documents that hadn't been touched for generations. He was beginning to give up hope when he suddenly let out a triumphant yell that echoed through the building, and brought Peggy running down.

"Sssh! You'll get me sacked!" she hissed.

"I think I've found what I need," chuckled Bobby. "But I'll keep my ideas to myself until I'm sure they will work. Tomorrow morning I must go to the park and see if Cowley is feeding the ducks."

He refused to say any more.

Later that evening Peggy told Joey what had happened.

"Whatever your brother plans to do, he'll have to work fast to stop trouble at tomorrow's match. And what has Adrian feeding the ducks got to do with it? We'll jolly well follow him, and try to find out."

The next morning, when Bobby left the house, Joey and Peggy were a few hundred yards behind him.

When he reached the park they saw him pause to read the notice on the railings of an enclosure which protected an ancient, but well-preserved, wooden pillory. The pillory, the notice explained, had been used in bygone days to punish law-breakers, who were fastened in it from sunrise to sunset so that passers-by could throw things at them.

Joey and Peggy saw Bobby stroll on to where Adrian was sitting on his usual seat, throwing stale bread to the ducks. They saw Adrian turn to Bobby with his usual charming smile. But then Bobby produced a sheet of paper, and began to talk sternly as he drew Adrian's attention to it.

The two youngsters were too far away to hear what Bobby was saying, but they saw his victim's beaming smile turn first into consternation and then to fury.

His gestures became threatening. Then he jumped to his feet and strode off in anger.

Bobby turned, and caught sight of Joey and Peggy watching.

"What was all that in aid of?" demanded Joey.

"I'll tell you after the match," Bobby promised mysteriously.

"But is Adrian going to cause **trouble** for the Blues?" Joey pleaded.

"We'll have to wait and see," Bobby replied.

They couldn't get another word out of him.

Bobby had still given no hint when he left for the stadium where he found Vic Crosby and the players excited and tense.

"There are **three** cattle trucks full of cows out in the car park," Vic told Bobby as he started to change, "and men with them, waiting for Cowley to arrive and give orders to turn them loose!"

"But he hasn't turned up yet, and I don't think he will," answered Bobby, as he pulled on his famous blue shirt.

"Can you be **sure** of that?" demanded Vic.

"No, we'll just have to wait and see," Bobby answered.

TENSE

THE fans gave Everpool a tremendous cheer as Bobby led them out, and cheered again when it was seen that they had won the toss.

Bobby could sense that his players were keyed-up and uneasy, and from the start he tried to force the pace of the game, in the hope they'd concentrate, and forget about Cowley and his threats.

But it didn't work.

The Blues were hesitant. Time and again they allowed Mandover to beat them to the ball. When they did gain possession their passes were ill-judged and went astray.

"**Get a grip, Blues! Get a grip!**" yelled the fans.

Bobby won the ball in a storming tackle and angled it to Tommy Keston, expecting him to make ground, but the winger allowed the ball to run past him. A Mandover defender made a mighty clearance,

When the pin-point centre came over, the Blues' skipper cracked an unstoppable overhead shot into the net.

and a good chance was lost.

But worse followed.

There was a moment's hesitation between Colin Jones and Harry Winters, when each left it to the other.

The alert Mandover striker took full advantage of the chance and, before they could stop him, his pile-driving shot was in the net.

"**Come on, Blues! What's wrong with you?**"

cried the fans. "**That one was a gift to Mandover!**"

Bobby trotted over indignantly to Tommy.

"That movement started when you let the ball run on," he challenged. "You were day-dreaming!"

"Sorry, Bobby," mumbled Tommy. "I was thinking about those wretched cows!"

Half-time came with the Blues still a goal down, and Bobby was all set to give his players a hard talking-to when he got them to the dressing-room. Then Vic burst in.

"The cattle trucks! They've gone! The men got fed up with waiting," he announced excitedly.

"Good," said Bobby. "Now perhaps we can concentrate on winning the match!"

Mandover opened the second-half feeling that they had a secure grip on the game.

But within a few minutes they were wondering what had hit them.

The Blues, eager to make amends, stormed down the pitch in top gear.

Don Westlake made a defence-splitting run, then crossed the ball to Peter Pitt, who cracked in a spectacular equaliser.

Mandover were still trying to recover from the shock, when Bobby chipped the ball into the goal-mouth and Don suddenly leapt in to head it under the bar.

The home fans went mad.

"**What a goal!**" they roared.

With Everpool two-one ahead, the visitors struggled in vain to recover their grip on the game. Tommy Keston drove in a screamer which the goalie only just managed to tip over the bar and then Colin Jones, coming through from defence, brought the goalie to his knees with a powerful shot that skimmed the turf all the way.

A third had to come—and it was Peter Pitt who set it up for Bobby to hook into the net to make the score three-one.

When the final whistle blew Don Westlake turned to his skipper.

"Out with it," he said. "What happened to Cowley?"

"He's left town. Everpool won't see him any more, because if he shows up again we can ask the mayor to stick him in the pillory," grinned Bobby.

"Whatever for?" gasped Don.

"Because he fed the ducks in the park," explained Bobby. "I decided to play him at his own game, and tried to find if there was some old, forgotten, unrepealed local law that I could catch him on. It seems that in the old days the park lake was Everpool's only source of drinking water. Anyone who contaminated it by throwing in scraps and rubbish could be punished by being put in the pillory for a whole day!"

"But surely a moth-eaten law of that sort could never be enforced?" frowned Don.

"We'll never know," chuckled Bobby. "**Cowley very wisely didn't wait to find out!**"

THE END

ENGLAND'S "SOCCER DON"

The man who found fame as both player and manager

IN April, 1974, Sir Alf Ramsey ended his 12-year reign as England's manager during which time he had led the side to World Cup triumph in 1966. We all knew it would be a difficult task to replace a man of such world-wide experience and it was some months before the F.A. announced the name of his successor—*Don Revie, one of the top three club managers in British football.*

"*It is the greatest honour any man could achieve*," said Don Revie when he heard of his appointment—and this from the man who had won almost everything in the game both as player and manager of Leeds United.

It was in 1946 that the tall, ambitious 18-year-old lad from Middlesbrough began his Football League career with Leicester City as a right-winger. In 1949 he had become the attacking schemer of the team that reached the F.A. Cup Final. Unfortunately he could not play in the Final owing to illness. But he made up for that disappointment in later years. He moved to Hull in 1949 and to Manchester City in 1951. Four years later, having

developed into a powerful centre-forward and goalgetter, Don gained his first England cap and helped to take City to Wembley for the F.A. Cup Final. The " Sky-Blues " were beaten by Newcastle, but within twelve months they were back at Wembley and this time Don Revie gained his winner's medal.

After a short spell with Sunderland he joined Leeds United in 1958—and within two years they were relegated to the Second Division. That sad day for United was really the start of Don's second career. He was appointed player-manager and in March, 1961, hung up his boots to concentrate on leading the side back to the top class. With his wonderful football brain, his determination and inspiring influence he turned Leeds United from " also-rans " into one of the greatest teams in the history of the game. In 1964 they returned to the upper form as Second Division Champions. It was a proud moment for the man who just ten years before had been voted " Footballer of the Year ".

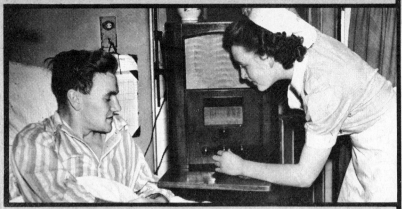

1949: Illness prevented Don turning out for Leicester City in the FA Cup Final, so here he listens to a broadcast of the match on the hospital radio. 1955: Footballer of the Year with Manchester City (below).

1956: Don gives his Man. City skipper a lift after victory in the Cup Final.

1957: Captain of Sunderland, having been transferred the previous year.

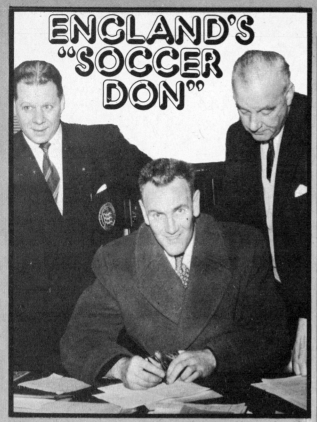

ENGLAND'S "SOCCER DON"

1958: Don's next move—to Elland Road, home of Leeds United—the team he was to make world-famous!

1961: Appointed manager of Leeds United, but Don still appeared in the first team from time to time.

During the years that have followed, the name of Don Revie has been headline news as the master-mind of a phenomenal team. Look at United's record since 1965: League Champions twice (1969 and '74), runners-up 5 times; F.A. Cup winners 1972 and three times losing Finalists; League Cup winners 1968; twice winners of the EUFA (Fairs) Cup (1968 and '71); European Cup-winners' Cup Finalists 1973.

SIDE OF THE CENTURY

IT is a remarkable record, a wonderful tribute to the man who built "the side of the century" and himself was three times voted "Manager of the Year". It was Don Revie who inspired the rise to world stardom of Billy Bremner, Jackie Charlton, Terry Cooper, Peter Lorimer, Paul Madeley, Mick Jones, Norman Hunter, Paul Reaney, Allan Clarke and David Harvey.

Jackie Charlton, now a successful club boss himself, has told how he almost gave up the game during his younger days because he felt he was making little progress. Then Don Revie took him in hand and turned him into one of the finest defenders in the League and 35 times an England international. Billy Bremner, too, has said many times that he owes everything to the man who put him on the road to fame.

You can imagine how the Leeds lads must have felt when they heard the news that Don Revie, the man they all so much respected and admired, the man for whom they would have played their hearts out, had accepted the invitation to become Sir Alf Ramsey's successor as manager of England's international squads. They were shattered—yet they were among the first to offer him their congratulations on his new honour.

As for Don himself, at the age of 48 he regarded the appointment as a new challenge—the beginning of a third career. First was his rise to international fame as a player; then his dedicated efforts to rescue struggling Leeds United and take them to the pinnacle of greatness, and thirdly his present task—to build a side worthy to represent England in the 1978 World Cup Finals to be held in Argentina. He succeeded in his first two aims—*can he achieve success in his third challenge?*

1969: Leeds first Championship success—and a record 67 points, too!

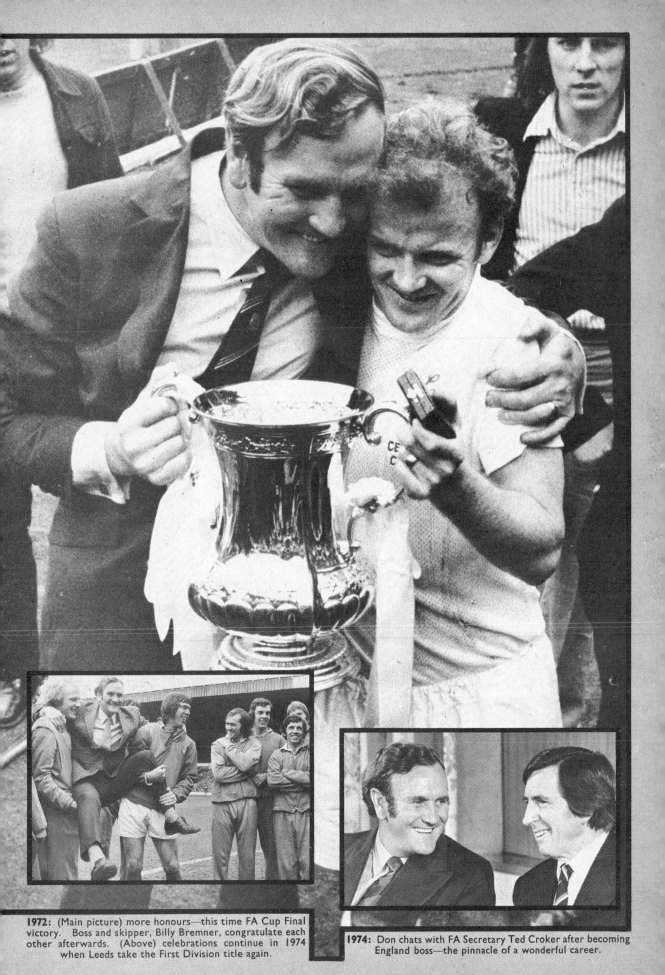

1972: (Main picture) more honours—this time FA Cup Final victory. Boss and skipper, Billy Bremner, congratulate each other afterwards. (Above) celebrations continue in 1974 when Leeds take the First Division title again.

1974: Don chats with FA Secretary Ted Croker after becoming England boss—the pinnacle of a wonderful career.

TOP TROPHIES

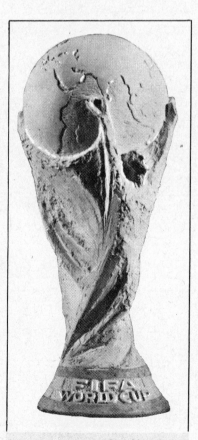

The Football League Cup.

SEASONS come and seasons go—so do players. Soccer undergoes many changes—but one thing never changes, the annual battle to win the game's top trophies and the fortunes that go with victory. Fame, too, for only winners are remembered, but then that's what the game is all about, isn't it? Football's trophies are the incentive.

The League Championship Cup (left), first won by Preston in 1889, and (above) the F.A. Cup which first appeared in 1911. It is the third F.A. Cup since 1872.

Youngest of all—the FIFA Trophy (World Cup) now held by W. Germany.

Know-All

He's Soccer's Mister Big-Head! See If You Can Catch Him Out.

ANSWERS BELOW

ONE OF THE LONGEST SERVING PLAYERS IN FOOTBALL TODAY IS HUGH McILMOYLE, PICTURED HERE IN HIS CARLISLE STRIP. I BET YOU DIDN'T KNOW THAT HUGHIE WAS IN LEICESTER CITY'S 1961 F.A. CUP FINAL SIDE!

1

2

WHEN LUTON TOWN RETURNED TO THE FIRST DIVISION IN 1974, ONE OF THEIR NEW RECRUITS WAS AUSTRALIAN WORLD CUP PLAYER, ADRIAN ALSTON. HERE'S ADRIAN ARRIVING IN ENGLAND WITH HIS WIFE AND BABY SON. UP "THE POTTERS"!

3

A GOOD TACKLE BY HOWARD KENDALL OF BIRMINGHAM ROBS WOLVERHAMPTON'S BARRY POWELL OF THE BALL! BOTH THESE SIDES HAVE WON THE FOOTBALL LEAGUE CUP — BIRMINGHAM IN 1965, WOLVES IN 1974!

YOU'RE WRONG THERE, KNOW-ALL!

THAT GOAL DOESN'T COUNT— IT WENT IN OFF THE REF!

I'M SORRY, BUT I'M AFRAID IT DOES!

GOAL!

4

WELSH INTERNATIONAL PLAYER, ASA HARTFORD, HAS BEEN A FANTASTIC SUCCESS SINCE HIS TRANSFER FROM WEST BROMWICH ALBION TO MANCHESTER CITY IN AUGUST, 1974. THERE ARE MORE HONOURS ON THE WAY FOR ASA!

5

IT MAKES A CHANGE!

Here's the one that got away—England boss Don Revie misses a "sitter" with the putter. Hard luck, Don!

The man with the cricket bat is John Hollins of Chelsea. The drive was a four all the way!

Ace soccer star Johann Cruyff tries his hand at tennis. *Over* the net in this game, Johann! But a change of sport is good relaxation.

England sharpshooters Colin Bell and Mick Channon are ready to hit the target in a different sport—pistol shooting.

World Champion boxer, John Conteh, picks up some points at football.

Even the rain showers at Fulham aren't *this* wet, Bobby Moore seems to be thinking as he gets soaked in a steeplechase event.

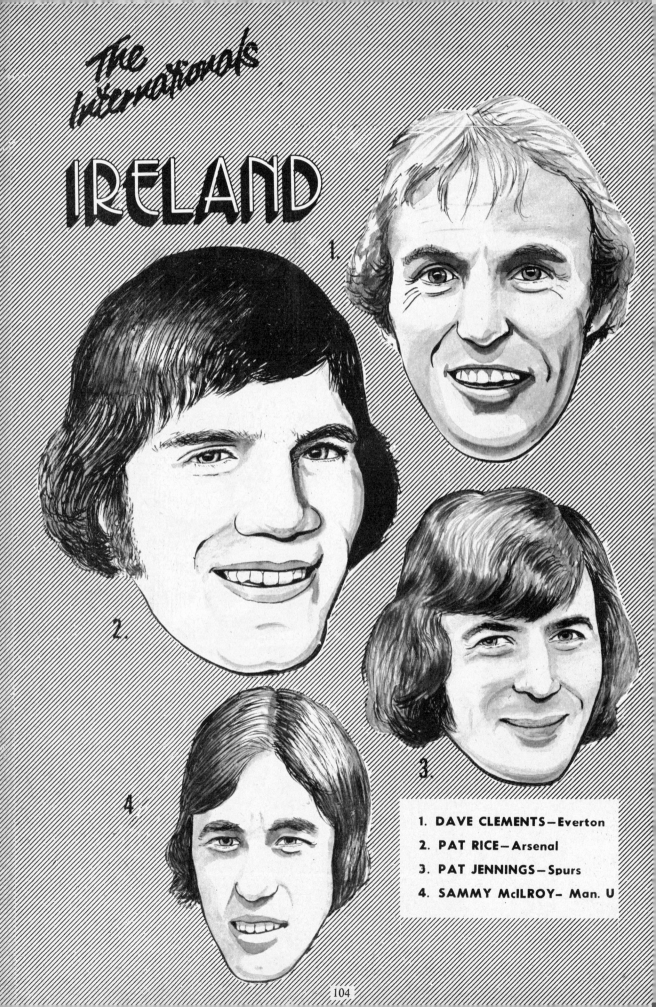

The Internationals

IRELAND

1. **DAVE CLEMENTS** — Everton
2. **PAT RICE** — Arsenal
3. **PAT JENNINGS** — Spurs
4. **SAMMY McILROY** — Man. U

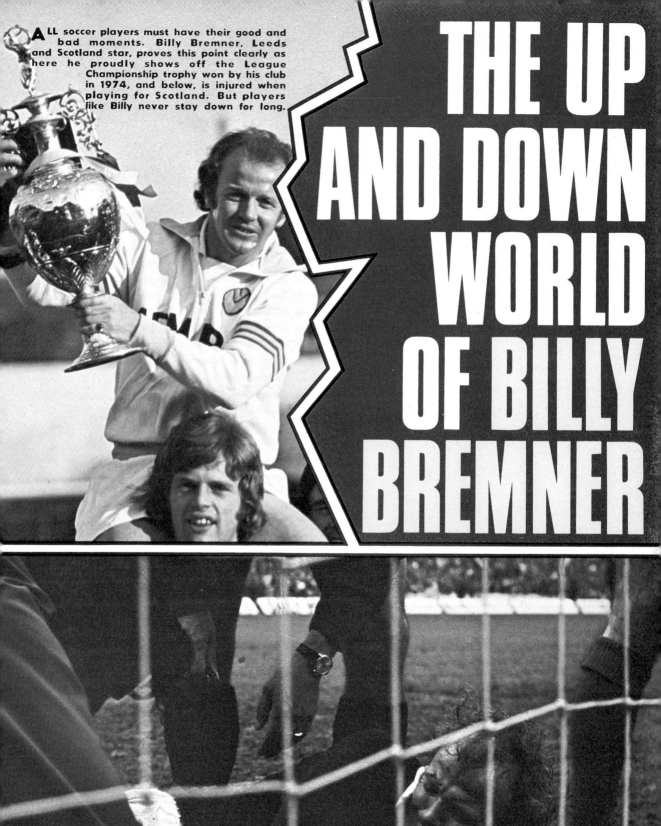

ALL soccer players must have their good and bad moments. Billy Bremner, Leeds and Scotland star, proves this point clearly as here he proudly shows off the League Championship trophy won by his club in 1974, and below, is injured when playing for Scotland. But players like Billy never stay down for long.

THE UP AND DOWN WORLD OF BILLY BREMNER

HAT-TRICK FOR ENGLAND'S

(1) Peter (white jersey), slips past West Germany's left-back on his way to goal. Now he is ready to shoot.

(3) The goalie makes a despairing dive, but he cannot do anything to prevent the ball from bouncing in.

for England Schoolboys.

WONDER BOY!

In June, 1974, England's Schoolboys beat West Germany 4-0 at Wembley, thanks mainly to 15-year-old Peter Coyne, who hit a hat-trick. This picture sequence shows how he got his brilliant third goal.

(2) As the West German defenders close in, the ball leaves the young striker's boot . . . bound for the net.

(4) It's there! Jubilant Peter turns away — to face his delighted team-mates and the happy crowd.

(6) Peter is also on Manchester United's staff. Let's hope he becomes a star with the "Red Devils", too!

OH, MY! WHAT A DIFFERENCE!

ASTON VILLA past and present. You all recognise the chap on the left—it's Charlie Aitken, Villa's long-service defender. Now take a long look at the fellow in the "outsize" shorts and thick woollen jersey. Dads and grandads may remember him for he is Johnny Dixon, Villa's captain when they won the F.A. Cup in 1957. You may not believe it but he's wearing the gear in which Villa became one of the greatest clubs in the game 50 years ago. Look at those boots, too. But in those days Villa were one of the smartest dressed teams in the League. You can laugh, but it's true, although no modern player would want to change back to that old-time kit!

BONNIE SCOTLAND

AT HOME...

Och aye! It's a goal! The scorer raising his arms in a joyful "V" for victory sign, is Kenny Burns, the exciting young Scot from Birmingham City. The match, against East Germany at Hampden Park in October, 1974, was only his second appearance as a full international, but he made the most of it with a snap-shot goal that put Scotland on the road to a well-merited 3–0 triumph.

...AND AWAY

Now it's the 1974 World Cup Finals when the Scots were unbeaten in their three Group 2 games—yet failed to reach the Quarter Finals on goal average. Here's a fine snap from Scotland's goalless draw with Brazil at Frankfurt with David Harvey (Leeds) making a flying save watched by defenders Martin Buchan and Jim Holton.

BELL
STRIKES TWICE

JUST before the start of the 1974–75 season, Do[n] Revie was appointed manager of England'[s] international teams after many successful year[s] with Leeds United. His first match as England'[s] boss was against Czechoslovakia at Wembley o[n] 30th October, 1974, a European Championshi[p]

With 10 minutes to go Colin flung himself feet forward at a low cross from Mike Channon. Although sprawling on his back he steered the ball into the net, much to the surprise of the Czech defenders. What a super goal it was—a "sitter"!

game. A crowd of 86,000 fans turned up to give support and encouragement to the new manager and his team—and how they needed it. Until well into the second-half the Czechs put up "an Iron Curtain" of defence against all attacks. It seemed that England would never score—but then Mike Channon headed a beauty past goalie Viktor. From then on there was no doubt about the result and the man who earned the biggest cheers at the finish was Colin Bell, Manchester City's "Mr. Perpetual Motion". He scored twice and these action shots show how he did it.

FOR ENGLAND!

A minute later England were three-up. The man who did it was—yes, Colin Bell. Again it was a perfect centre from Mike Channon and this time "Dinger" Bell leapt above two defenders and nodded the ball into the Czech net. Well done!

ON THE BALL with

BRIAN MOORE

The man respected by the football stars he commentates on.

ON THE BALL

THE BIG MATC

THOSE of you who watch television—and who doesn't, these days?—will need no introduction to Brian Moore. The genial commentator and the man who runs the "On the Ball" and "The Big Match" programmes every weekend is as well-known—perhaps better known—than many of the Soccer stars he presents to the viewing public. To say he's popular would be an understatement. Brian is a real student of the game—and has been since the days when he was a newspaper reporter and later a radio match-commentator. Players, managers and fans respect him for his knowledge and understanding of football and his friendly approach to his difficult job.

But Brian Moore is not just a week-end television star. Whenever football is "on the box" you can be sure Brian will be there—internationals, mid-week Cup games and, of course, the World Cup Finals. When you see his smiling face appear on the screen you may think he has just walked into the studio for a friendly natter about the game he loves as much as we do. You'd be wrong. A great deal of preparation is needed before even the shortest programme and we can prove it. Our cameraman joined Brian at the start of a typical Saturday and followed him around. You, too, can join Brian in this interesting series of pictures—and remember, this all happens BEFORE he prepares his Sunday afternoon "Big Match" presentation.

.00 Brian arrives at the London Weekend T.V. Centre to discuss the day's programme with Editor Mike Archer.

10.30 Now he's in the cutting room with Mike Archer and one of the camera staff watching a snatch of film he will talk about later in his "On the Ball" spot.

1.00 Time now for a visit to the World of Sport studio to check up on the latest sporting news in the Press.

10.00 Meanwhile, the "Big Match" technicians are getting down to work at White Hart Lane for the Spurs' match later that afternoon.

113

11.15 Back in the studio, Brian is still hard at work. Here he is checking over with his personal secretary his revised script for his lunchtime "On the Ball" chat.

11.30 Everything is now ready for the "run through"—or at least, it should be, so Brian takes a last glance at his script. There must be no hitch when the programme starts.

11.35 Now Dickie Davies, who is responsible for the popular programme, has a last brief word with Brian. They're great pals.

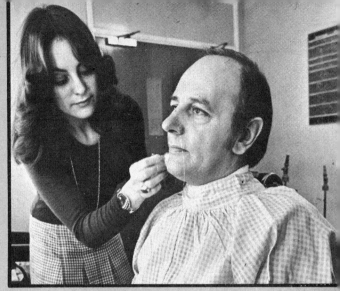

11.40 No, Brian's not having a quick haircut before appearing in front of the cameras. Just a touch of make-up from the expert.

11.55 Everything's ready and Brian is in his seat waiting for the signal to begin the all-important rehearsal.

11.55 Here's the control room where Mike Archer (centre) watches and times Brian's run-through on the panel of monitor screens.

12.40 At last, all the preparations completed, Brian waits for the signal that he is "on the air". Now it's the real thing.

13.00 Meanwhile, at White Hart Lane in North London, the fans are beginning to arrive for the game. Brian will soon join them.

14.00

After a quick lunch and a fast car ride, Brian reports for duty at Tottenham ready for the game with Birmingham. First he tests out his equipment up on his commentary position.

15.00 Once the game starts Brian begins his commentary, for even though it is not "live", his report is taped.

15.00

Let's spare a thought for the camera crews who have been on duty from early morning erecting and testing their equipment. Then from kick-off to final whistle they must be "on the ball" capturing every match incident.

17.00 Now the game is over and Brian's expert commentary has been recorded on tape at the studio. But he still has time for an after-match interview with Kenny Burns, the Birmingham star.

17.30 His job finished, Brian Moore can now relax after returning to the studio, but the camera crews and the technicians must pack up all their equipment before their day's work is over.

Royal's Rangers

Part 2

CONTINUED FROM PAGE 55

THE HOME TEAM KICKED-OFF...

THEY LOOK AS IF THEY MEAN REAL BUSINESS! THEY DIDN'T LIKE THE LICKING WE GAVE THEIR OTHER SIDE!

TICUARDA! TICUARDA!

THEY'RE ON TOP FORM, TOO! THEY'LL TAKE SOME BEATING!

ONCE AGAIN, BIG JIM BLACKER FOUND HIMSELF FACING THE ASSAULT VIRTUALLY ALONE...

GET IT FROM HIM, JIM!

DIRK NIPPED IN TO GIVE ME A HAND THE LAST TIME THIS HAPPENED! BUT I'M ON MY OWN THIS TIME!

THE BURLY FULL-BACK FLASHED A SCOWLING GLANCE AT THE YELLING CROWD...

JIM! FOR PETE'S SAKE... WATCH IT!

IT'S THE BLOKE WHO WAS CLIMBING THE HOSPITAL WALL THE OTHER DAY! WHAT'S HE DOING WITH DIRK?

DIRK McKEE GAVE A WEARY SIGN...

I AM THE DOCTOR EMPLOYED BY SENOR PANCHEZ TO RE-DRESS YOUR SHOULDER! IF YOU WOULD COME WITH ME...

HOOTS, MON! WHAT A TIME TO PICK! BUT... I SUPPOSE I HAVE TO!

BIG JIM GASPED AS HE WATCHED DIRK AND THE STRANGER MOVE AWAY THROUGH THE CROWD...

HE... HE'S TAKING DIRK WITH HIM! THEY'RE LEAVING THE STAND!

JIM! LOOK OUT!

THEN IT WAS THE TURN OF BOTH PLAYERS AND SPECTATORS TO GASP...

JIM'S RUNNING OFF THE FIELD!

CARAMBA!

THERE'S SOMETHING WRONG THERE! I KNOW IT! SURE AS MY NAME'S BLACKER... DIRK'S IN SOME KIND OF DANGER!

TRIO

GOALKEEPER 'DOUGHNUT' DONOVAN WAS TOO ASTOUNDED TO BE AT HIS BEST, AND...

OLÉ GO-ALLL!

WHAT THE BLAZES IS HE THINKING OF?

MANAGER BEN ROYAL WAS TEARING HIS HAIR OUT...

BLACKER LET HIM THROUGH! HE LET THEM SCORE THAT GOAL! I'LL HAVE HIS CONTRACT IN SHREDS FOR THIS!

TRULY, SENOR ROYAL... THE WAYS OF ENGLISH FOOTBALLERS ARE QUITE REMARKABLE!

SENOR ROYAL... WHERE ARE YOU GOING?

AFTER THE PERISHER, THAT'S WHERE!

AS THE RANGERS' MANAGER DASHED INTO THE STREET...

STOP! COME BACK HERE!

I'M TOO LATE! IF-IF ONLY THERE WAS A PERISHIN' TAXI SOMEWHERE AROUND!

DOWN TO TEN MEN, CAXFORD WERE REALLY UP AGAINST IT...

HERE THEY COME AGAIN!

TICUARDA! TICUARDA!

DESPERATELY, CAXFORD FELL BACK ON DEFENCE...

DARN IT!

THEY'VE PASSED TO THEIR WINGER! AND THERE'S NO ONE TO MARK HIM!

GALLANTLY, GOALKEEPER DOUGHNUT DONOVAN LEAPT FOR THE SHOT, BUT...

BRAVO TICUARDA!

GO-AALL!

THAT PUTS THEM TWO UP!

INSIDE-RIGHT GLOOMY DAY GAVE A GROAN OF DESPAIR TO CAPTAIN ROD ROPER...

I COULD'VE TOLD YOU! IT WAS ALL IN MY HOROSCOPE FOR THE DAY...WE'RE GOING TO GET WELL AND TRULY CLOBBERED!

WHAT DO YOU EXPECT? WITH DIRK OUT OF THE TEAM...AND NOW JIM JUST TAKING OFF! WHERE IN THE BLAZES HAS HE GOT TO?

AT THAT MOMENT, JUST OUTSIDE THE CITY, JIM BLACKER HAD THUMBED A LIFT...

FOLLOW THAT CAR! IT COULD BE A MATTER OF LIFE OR DEATH!

CARAMBA! IT IS ONE OF THE INGLISI FOOTBALLERS!

FASTER! WE MUSTN'T LOSE THEM! I'LL PAY YOU WHATEVER YOU WANT LATER... BUT FOR PETE'S SAKE, KEEP UP WITH THEM!

I THINK ALL ENGLISHMEN MUST BE MAD! THIS ONE SHOULD BE PLAYING FOOTBALL... HE SHOULD NOT BE HERE AT ALL!

121

I REGRET HE WILL NOT BE ABLE TO REMOVE HIS DRESSINGS FOR MANY DAYS YET... BUT OTHERWISE HE IS QUITE WELL!

H'MM, WELL, IF JIM BLACKER ISN'T HERE, I MAY AS WELL TAKE DIRK BACK WITH ME TO SEE THE REST OF THE MATCH!

BUT YOU WAIT TILL I GET HOLD OF HIM! HE'D BETTER HAVE A DARNED GOOD EXCUSE, OR I'LL RUN HIM OUT OF THE RANGERS!

AH CANNA UNDERSTAND JIM DOIN' SUCH A THING! OCH, I BET THE RANGERS ARE HAVIN' A REET POOR TIME OF IT!

BACK AT THE STADIUM THE SCORE HAD REACHED THREE-NIL...

GOAL! TICUARDA!

WE DON'T STAND AN EARTHLY! THE REST OF THE LADS HAVE HALF THEIR MINDS ON WHAT'S HAPPENED TO JIM!

GRIMLY ROD ROPER TRIED TO INSTILL NEW CONFIDENCE INTO HIS MEN...

COME ON, RANGERS, LET'S GO!

EVERYONE UP! THERE'S NOT TIME ENOUGH TO PLAY DEFENSIVELY! IT'S GOT TO BE SCORE OR LOSE!

TWICE THE ALL-OUT TACTICS PROVED SUCCESSFUL...

GO-ALL! MAYBE WE CAN JUST FORCE AN EQUALISER!

IT'S THERE! GOOD OLD ROD!

BUT EVEN AS ROD BROKE THROUGH FOR A THIRD TIME...

PHEEE-EEEEP!

BRAVO! TICUARDA!

WE'VE LOST! AND IT'S ALL BLACKER'S FAULT! JUST WAIT TILL I SEE HIM AGAIN!

BUT BEN ROYAL DID NOT KNOW THAT THE CHANCES WERE... *HE WOULD NEVER SEE JIM AGAIN*...

YOU SHOULD NOT HAVE MEDDLED, INGLISI! NOW I SHALL RETURN WITH YOUR FRIENDS TO ENGLAND... AND REMOVE THE JEWELS FROM MCKEE'S BANDAGES!

HAVING, IN THIS WAY, SUCCESSFULLY SMUGGLED THEM OUT OF TICUARDA UNDER THE PRESIDENTO'S NOSE!

BUT *YOU*, MY MEDDLING FRIEND, WILL *NOT* BE WITH US *WHEN WE LAND IN ENGLAND!*

AT THE STADIUM THE TEAMS WERE JUST LEAVING THE FIELD...

TICUARDA! TICUARDA!

THEY WOULDN'T HAVE RAISED A CHEER IF *WE'D WON!* WONDER WHY THEY DISLIKE US SO MUCH?

IT'S A MYSTERY TO ME! BUT RIGHT NOW BEN ROYAL HAS GOT A MAN-SIZE *DISLIKE* FOR *JIM BLACKER!*

THE CAXFORD MANAGER WAS FURIOUS...

OCH, THERE MUST BE A REASON FOR WHAT JIM DID, BEN!

THERE'D BETTER BE, DIRK! RUNNING OFF THE FIELD LIKE THAT IN THE MIDDLE OF A GAME! YOU JUST WAIT 'TILL HE SHOWS UP AGAIN...

BUT SENOR PANCHEZ INTENDED THAT THE RANGER WAS NEVER TO BE SEEN ALIVE AGAIN...

I MUST RETURN TO THE PRESIDENTO! I WILL LEAVE *YOU* TO DEAL WITH THIS MEDDLING GRINGO!

DO NOT WORRY, SENOR PANCHEZ! WE WILL ENSURE THAT HE MEETS WITH A MOST REGRETTABLE ...ER... ACCIDENT!

THE MINISTER'S MEN DROVE JIM TO THE TOP OF A CANYON...

YOU ARE ABOUT TO MAKE YOUR LAST JOURNEY, GRINGO! FROM HERE ALL THE WAY *DOWN* TO THE BOTTOM!

THEN WE WILL GO DOWN AND CUT THE ROPES FROM YOUR WRISTS! IT WILL BE BELIEVED THAT YOU TRIPPED AND *FELL* TO YOUR *DOOM!*

123

I'LL TELL YOU ALL ABOUT IT, BEN... AFTER I'VE MADE SURE THIS CREEP DOESN'T *SCARPER OFF!*

UUUGH!

THEN JIM REACHED FOR HIS FRIEND, DIRK McKEE...

HE'S *CRAZY!* STOP HIM!

AND I'VE GOT NEWS FOR YOU, DIRK! YOUR SHOULDER'S ALMOST *HEALED* UP! YOU DON'T *NEED* THOSE BANDAGES ON AT ALL!

BUT AS DIRK'S BANDAGES UNRAVELLED...

THE *STATE JEWELS!*

THAT'S RIGHT! BUT DON'T THINK POOR OLD DIRK HERE HAD ANYTHING TO DO WITH HIDING THEM! HE *DIDN'T EVEN KNOW* THEY WERE THERE!

PANCHEZ PLANNED TO RETURN TO ENGLAND WITH US, TOGETHER WITH HIS PHONEY DOCTOR! ONCE IN ENGLAND THEY WOULD HAVE CHANGED DIRK'S DRESSING... AND, OF COURSE, POCKETED WHAT WAS INSIDE... *THE JEWELS!*

SACRAMENTO! A *PERFECT* PLAN FOR SMUGGLING THEM OUT OF TICUARDA!

FREE FROM HIS HAMPERING BANDAGES, DIRK FLEXED HIS INJURED SHOULDER...

HE HAD *ME* FOOLED, TOO! STICK A WEE PLASTER ON MA SHOULDER... AND I CAN *PLAY!*

THAT'S RIGHT, DIRK! FOR CAXFORD'S LAST MATCH WE'LL BE AT FULL STRENGTH!

AND SO, TWO DAYS LATER...

BRAVO, INGLISI!

LOVELY KICK, JIM! RIGHT TO DIRK'S FEET!

GOT IT, JIM LADDIE!

IT WAS A HARD, CLEAN GAME... WITH BRILLIANT GOALS FROM BOTH SIDES...

IT'S *THERE*! NICE WORK, DIRK!

THEY'VE EQUALISED! AND WITH PLAY LIKE THAT THEY *DESERVE* TO!

BUT IT WAS RANGERS' SKIPPER ROD ROPER WHO SLAMMED HOME THE WINNING GOAL...

IT'S IN! GO-ALLL!

BRAVO, INGLISI!

ALL OF A SUDDEN THE FANS *LIKE* US, ROD. THE TICUARDIANS ARE PROVING THEMSELVES REAL SPORTSMEN!

AND UP UNTIL THIS GAME THEY *HATED* US! THERE MUST BE A REASON!

THERE WAS.

MY POOR PEOPLE HAVE BEEN ROBBED AND CHEATED FOR MONTHS BY THE TRAITOR PANCHEZ! THEY DID NOT REALISE I KNEW NOTHING ABOUT SUCH THINGS!

AND AS PANCHEZ WAS THE ONE WHO *INVITED US* HERE... FOR HIS OWN ENDS... THEY BELIEVED WE WERE *FRIENDS* OF HIS! NOW I *DO* UNDERSTAND!

A THIEF AND TRAITOR HAS BEEN BROUGHT TO JUSTICE! THE PEOPLE OF TICUARDA ARE *HAPPY* AGAIN! AND IT IS ALL THANKS TO THE GREAT CAXFORD RANGERS... AND TO *SENOR JIM BLACKER* IN PARTICULAR!

AND SO, BEN ROYAL CAME TO THE END OF THE JIM BLACKER STORY...

SO YOU SEE! STUBBORN AS A MULE THOUGH JIM MAY BE, WE WOULDN'T HAVE HIM ANY OTHER WAY!

The End

You're Never Too Old!

THEY say football is a young man's game. But it is still remarkable how often the headlines are stolen by the "Peter Pan" players . . . the long service men who seem to have been around for years.

In fact, the teenage stars often find themselves overshadowed by players who make a mockery of the veteran label. Of course, youth is the lifeblood of soccer and, in Scotland at any rate, young men have taken a grip of the managerial scene and naturally players are getting big breaks much earlier . . . from 15 years of age upwards.

But tribute should be paid to the long service men in Scotland. There's Celtic's Billy McNeill for example; John Greig of Rangers; Doug Smith of Dundee United; John Cushley of Dumbarton; Alec Kinninmonth of Dunfermline and John Markie of Falkirk. The list is long and impressive and it is always noticeable that the older stars hold down the captain's role.

Experience

THE sport is still dominated by the younger players, of course, but without doubt the character would disappear without the experience from the old-timers. Once upon a time, British football seemed to be the sole property of players over the age of 25 and managers over the age of 45. Not so today. The gap between player and boss has vanished without trace and there are cases where a player can actually be older than the man in the manager's chair!

The game is claimed to be for young men, but with a matter of ten years spanning teenage stars and managers, how does one work out how old is old? It always seems comical when reports pin-point the efforts of a veteran player of, say 30 years of age, and yet in the same feature the young manager of 35 is mentioned.

With men like Bobby Charlton playing and managing it must be very hard to find the suitable description . . . but they thankfully seem to go on for ever.

Alec Kinninmonth of Dunfermline (above) and two other fine long service men (below), Doug Smith of Dundee United and Celtic's Billy McNeill shake hands before the 1974 Scottish F.A. Cup Final

John Markie, above, a Falkirk player for 11 seasons.

This unique series of action snaps shows a sensational goal scored by Brian Kidd for Arsenal against Everton at Goodison Park. The ``Blues'' were one-up when the ``Gunners'' were awarded a free-kick.

THROUGH

It was just outsi the penalty area so the Evert chaps formed a wall between Brian and their own ´keeper. It looked impossible for the ball to beat that human barrier — but it did !

THE WALL !

Brian Kidd hit a fantastic shot that curled in the air through a gap in the wall and was in the net before goalie Dave Lawson could move to it — a real banana shot that ``kidded'' the Everton defence.

The Internationals WALES

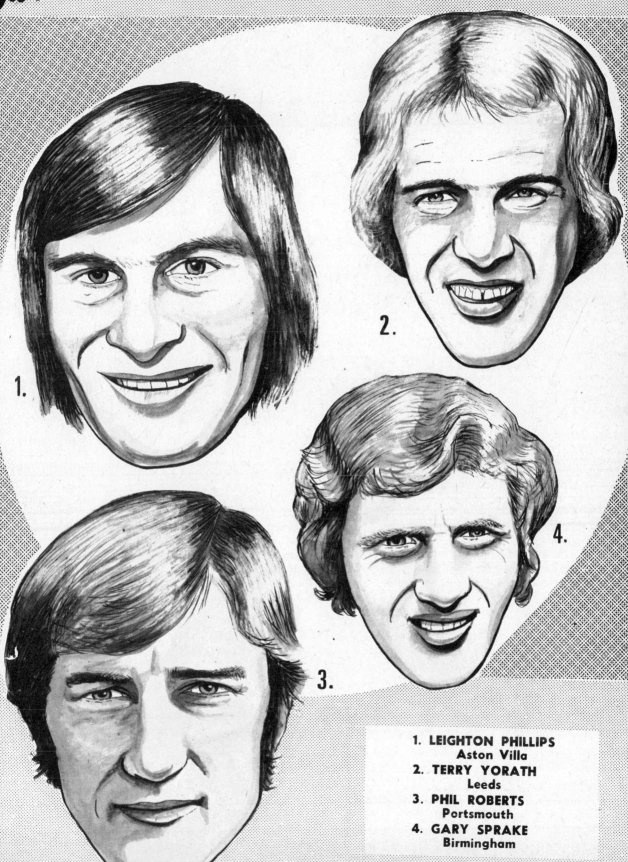

1. **LEIGHTON PHILLIPS**
   Aston Villa
2. **TERRY YORATH**
   Leeds
3. **PHIL ROBERTS**
   Portsmouth
4. **GARY SPRAKE**
   Birmingham

LAGS

"**W**HAT have we got here, then?** Prisoner Willie Smith lying around dozing in the sun. Thinks this is a perishin' holiday camp, does he?"

The harsh voice of **"Bad-News"** Benson, Governor of Grimwalls Prison, awoke Willie Smith from a pleasant snooze. He had been resting in the sun with his back against a tree and a sheet of paper and a pencil fell from his lap as he sat up sharply.

"Ah, Mr. Benson, sir," he said smoothly. "I was deep in thought, Governor. Didn't hear you coming. I was just engaging in some time and motion study—er —seeing if we could streamline the movements of the team a bit better."

"You're doing **time**, Smith, and I'll see you'll be put into **motion**," guffawed the stiff-backed, beady-eyed Bad-News. "You're supposed to be out there training and coaching the team . . . and playing as their skipper. You've wangled lots of special privileges because I have a soft spot for the Lags Eleven, haven't you? On your feet, Smith, and let me see you take at least one kick at the ball. **Move!**"

Sighing, Willie pocketed his piece of paper and trotted over to join the grinning prison soccer team. Known as **"Brilliant Genius"** for the crafty way in which he had run the team and made it famous in the prison league, Willie knew just how far he could go with the soccer-mad Governor.

"Give us the ball," he muttered to **"Nut-Case"** Norris, "and let me put on a show for old razor-eyes."

Grinning, the big centre-forward slipped the ball to his skipper. Brilliant Genius did a smart bit of dribbling, and banged in a shot which **"Monkey-Grab"** Miller, in goal, allowed to beat him.

"Nice work, Smith," called Bad-News, hands behind his back, teetering backwards and forwards on his heels. "But you wouldn't have found it so easy if the rest of those lazy layabouts had been trying. Come over here, you oily-tongued con man."

"Flattery'll get you nowhere, Bad-News," muttered Brilliant Genius, strolling over to the Governor.

"I've got plans for you, Smith," rapped Bad-News Benson, smiling nastily. **"You're leaving Grimwalls Prison!"**

For once Brilliant Genius was shattered. "What? You mean I'm going outside?"

"No, I'm not going to release you on an unsuspecting public," jeered the Governor, while the team drifted over to hear what was said, all obviously

ELEVEN

shaken by the shattering news.

"You mean I'm going to another jail?" gasped Brilliant Genius. "But, Mr. Bad-News . . . I mean Mr. Benson, **sir** . . . you **can't** do that! What would Lags Eleven do without me?"

"Haw, haw!" roared Bad-News. "Had you twittering then, didn't I, Smith? Fact is, you're being seconded on special duties to Brimstone Jail. I've promised the Governor, my old pal Commander Twerpe-Trimble, that you'd start a soccer team for him and train 'em up to league standards. Sooner that's done, the sooner you'll be back in your cosy quarters here."

"'Ere, what are we gonna do without Brilliant to see us through?" demanded Nut-Case Norris.

"You'll be acting captain till he comes back, Norris," barked Bad-News. "Pack your gear, Smith. You'll be leaving in an hour."

UNDER ORDERS

BRIMSTONE JAIL was an ancient stone building built like a castle, surrounded by a moat and huge tracts of marsh and lakes.

"Splendid place for a jail," enthused Bad-News. "A man would have to be a frog to get away from here."

"Or a crocodile, like you," Brilliant Genius said under his breath.

Inside the large clanging gates they passed a big pool full of model boats of all kinds.

"Commander Twerpe-Trimble's hobby," said Bad-News. "He can never forget his many years at sea."

In the office they were greeted by the chief warder, a huge man with a face that looked as if it had been carved out of rock.

Slam! Slam! His boots crashed on to the hard floor as he flung up a smart salute to Bad-News Benson.

"Welcome to Brimstone . . . sah!" he barked. "Commander's compliments, and he's in his workshop." He glanced at Brilliant Genius, small pale eyes boring holes through him. "Wot's this then, Mr. Benson?"

"He may not look much, Narker," chuckled Bad-News. "Miserable-looking specimen he might be . . . but he has a way with soccer teams."

"Hurr, he don't look as if he can whip much sense into the bunch of layabouts we've got here, Mr. Benson. Right bunch o' wilting flowers they are. But I've heard he's done wonders with your lot, Lags

Eleven, so I'll give him the benefit of the doubt. Follow me, sir, and you, Smith."

The Governor's workshop was full of activity. It was a large boatshed near the prison walls, and inside Brilliant saw a slipway leading down to a huge, ancient old iron watergate, with water gleaming beyond.

A full-sized yacht was being finished and painted on the slipway, with convicts working busily under the eye of a mild looking silver-haired man.

Commander Twerpe-Trimble introduced himself and explained to Bad-News and Brilliant Genius.

"The Commissioners—hah—feel the prisoners here don't get enough—um—healthy exercise," he murmured, absent-mindedly, his gaze on the yacht. "Poppycock, of course, but they want me to start a football team. Fact is, Benson, I spent so many years at sea I don't know much about—um—soccer. No room to play it on the decks of my small ships, y'see. That's why I asked for your assistance."

"My man Smith here, Commander," said Bad-News importantly, "will muster a team and whip 'em into shape. He knows what's good for him. He'll stay here until Brimstone has a team that'll hold its own with the best of 'em. They'll not be up to the standard of the Lags Eleven, but Smith will do his best."

"Splendid—excellent," Twerpe-Trimble was saying. "Chief Warder Narker will give every assistance, Mr. Benson. He's already collected the—er—gear. So it's up to this young feller here. Full command, my dear chap," he said to Brilliant Genius. **"But I expect results."**

"I'll soak Bad-News for some extra privileges for this little lot," muttered Brilliant Genius. "From what Narker says, **I'm going to be mighty unpopular with the Brimstone prisoners."**

WELCOME PARTY

WILLIE found Narker's team selection in the Recreation Room. None looked like "wilting flowers"—they seemed a tough crowd to him.

They looked at him mildly when Narker roared: "Pay attention there! This is the chap who's gonna teach you to play football."

Amazed, Willie saw that the men were playing snakes and ladders, table tennis and draughts. Some were watching a nursery programme on the television and others were busy sewing. But his eyes glittered as he saw they were making sections of sails. Narker marched out, and suddenly one of the sailmakers spoke:

"Forget it, mate. We don't play rough games like football."

"We came 'ere to do our stretch and take things easy. Build up our strengths for when we get back to our capers outside."

A big man with a jaw like a leg of lamb got up, strolled over and lifted Willie off the floor by both shoulders of his jacket.

"I ain't planning to get a busted ankle kicking a little ball around," he snarled. "I watch blokes on the telly gettin' **paid** for doing that. Me do it for free? Nuts! I got other plans."

"Like making up to the Guv and preparing sails for his boat?" said Willie. "Then sawing through that iron gate and sailing away when the yacht's finished?"

The jaw jammed against Willie's and he trembled. " 'Ere, 'oo told yer that?"

"Just g-guessed," stammered Willie. "It's what I'd do myself if I wanted to get out of Brimstone. Me being a good sailor, like."

The rest of the Brimstone prisoners got up and crowded round him. "Hey, you know how to handle a yacht—do all the navigatin', get through all that flippin' maze o' waterways out there?"

"Sure," said Brilliant boldly. "I had me own boat once, in better days." He didn't add that it had been a rowing boat when he had lived near the River Thames. "Take you anywhere you want to go. Me, I fancy South America."

"He's conning us," growled Jawbone.

"No, he ain't," yelled a voice from the doorway. "Willie . . . Willie Smith! **Brilliant Genius!"**

The newcomer, a burly squat man with a bald head, big ears, a turned-up nose and merry little eyes, bounced into the room and danced Willie around.

"Porky! Porky Trotter!" yelled Brilliant delightedly.

"Ain't seen Brilliant since I played in the Darkmoor Prison team against his Lags Eleven," said Porky Trotter. "Boys, I'l ltell you all about his exploits."

As Porky Trotter talked, Jawbone reached out a massive hand.

"Okay, pal. We put on a show of learning soccer and then, when that boat's ready, **we sail away under your command."**

Porky looked thoughtful, and doubtful. He spoke quickly.

Chief warder Narker was amazed! There, in front of him, his prison team performed incredible skills.

"Boy, I miss my soccer. Since I came here I haven't had a game of lovely football."

"Okay, you're skipper and goalie," said Willie instantly. "I'll be manager an' playing coach. Get the gear from Narker and let's get goin'."

When the two were alone, Porky asked Willie: "Say, you ain't serious about breakin' out o' here? You don't want to leave your cushy number at Grimwalls . . . and Lags Eleven?"

"No fear," Brilliant Genius grinned. "But I can't leave here till I get a soccer team going, and then I'll think of something to get out from under—double quick. That Jawbone joker is a bit above my fighting weight . . . and besides, he might break me glasses."

ESCAPE

CHIEF WARDER NARKER could not believe his eyes. Brilliant Genius and the team were doing ball training, with Porky Trotter enjoying himself in goal. The swift passes, nifty dribbling and powerful shots amazed him.

Narker reported to the Governor, who was busy fighting a naval battle with his model boats on the pond.

"That new boy Smith is a genius . . . **sah**," he reported with a salute that nearly knocked his cap off. "He's got those layabouts playing football that'd beat any World Cup team."

"Splendid," muttered Commander Twerpe-Trimble. "I'll telephone Benson and get him to bring Lags Eleven up for a game. Interestin', what, to see whether Smith can beat his own team?"

The news came to Willie a few days later. "All turn out in your gear at 14·30 hours!" roared Narker. "We've got a visiting team to give you a game. Lags Eleven, **your** famous team, Smith."

Willie had hardly recovered when Bad-News Benson arrived in a coach carrying Nut-Case Norris and the rest of the team, together with some warders to watch over them on the journey.

"You place me in a difficult position, Mr. Benson, sir," Brilliant Genius complained. **"I've now got to play against the team I've trained."**

"On the contrary, Smith," said Bad-News with an oily smile, "you will lead the **Brimstone** team. We shall see whether **you** are responsible for the success of Lags Eleven, or **myself!**"

"Play against me own mob?" howled Brilliant. "It won't do, Mr. Benson. It just won't do."

"I disagree," smirked Bad-News. "If you have trained Brimstone to the standard I expect, you have nothing to fear. I look forward to a cracking game."

Jawbone took Brilliant aside in the dressing-room to add to his worries.

"One of the boys has cut through them bars in the boatshed," he whispered hoarsely. "We're ready to go as soon as the game's over. Old Twirpy's throwing a party to celebrate his football team so you be ready to slip out wiv us when the shindig's going full blast."

"Oh, no," groaned Willie. "Old Narker'll be watching us like a hawk."

"We'll take care of 'im," grinned Jawbone. "He's the ref, ain't he? A little accident, all in the spirit of the game, see?"

Brilliant Genius knew he had to act fast.

"Just going for a little trot, Jawbone," he said, hastily tying his bootlaces. "Always like to limber up before a game."

Willie trotted round the ground—a rough patch within the prison walls. But after two circuits, he veered direction to go round the governor's garden. Here there was plenty of cover from trees and shrubs, and within seconds he had eased himself through an open window of the nearby boatshed.

Thoughtfully he eyed the finished yacht. "All ready for launching," he muttered. "Now what can I do? I can't grass on these Brimstone lads. If I refuse to go with 'em, they'll duff me up . . . and if I **do** go with 'em I'll have twenty more years of Bad-News Benson! **Cor, what a spot to be in!**"

CRUNCH GAME

BUT Willie got to work and soon he was back in the dressing-room, greeting Lags Eleven, before the start of the game.

"Haw, haw! Lags Eleven," Jawbone guffawed, as the two teams ran out. "Champs, eh? Us Brimstone lads'll run yer into the ground!"

Brilliant had decided on being skipper of Brimstone and it was he who took the toss with Nut-Case Norris.

There was no wind, so Brilliant elected to take the half which gave a slight downhill advantage on the sloping pitch.

Chief Officer Narker lumbered around as referee like a buffalo trying to control a game that soon became fast and bruising. It was plain he knew little of the rules, and both teams took advantage of this ignorance.

Bang! Explosive action when Brilliant Genius played football against his own pals!

Bad-News Benson, jumping up and down with rage, shouted furiously from the touchline.

"Where's your rule-book, ref? Cor, he's got no control!"

On the pitch Willie passed to Jawbone as he saw Nut-Case Norris rushing in to intercept. Like a tank Jawbone lumbered forward. He met Nut-Case face to face, and two large feet slammed at the ball simultaneously.

Bang! Caught between the battering-ram boots, the ball burst.

Narker ran up, blowing his whistle furiously. "Darn it, what now?" he muttered.

"New ball, ref," said Brilliant. "Then you drop it on this spot, see?"

"All right," snarled Narker. "Think I don't know anything, Smith?"

A spare ball was found and a player from both sides joined Narker as he prepared to bounce up.

Jawbone nudged Brilliant. "This is our chance to get rid o' Narker," he muttered hoarsely. **"Crowd in, boys."**

As the ball hit the ground the referee disappeared in a crush of bodies. **"Slippery"** Stan, a Brimstone forward, eased out of the scrum with the ball, and the bodies broke apart. The Chief Officer was still lying on the ground.

"Stop the game!" bawled Bad-News Benson, running on to the pitch. "Get that man off. I'm taking over as ref."

"Watch it now, Jawbone," hissed Brilliant. "With Bad-News as ref, he'll have you in his book if you so much as give him an insolent look. You've gotta play to the rules now."

"Who cares?" grinned Jawbone. "We got rid of Narker, didn't we?"

Brilliant Genius's heart sank. The secret part of his plan would now have to be brought into operation. It meant trouble for him, but he hoped to be well away from Brimstone before the full force hit home.

Under Bad-News' beady eye, the game became a model of manners. Brilliant's Brimstone team showed they could behave themselves, and Lags Eleven responded. Hardened wrong-doers were actually seen bowing to each other politely if they so much as touched another player.

"Splendid, splendid," beamed Bad-News as Willie passed him. "You've done well, Smith, though I say it myself."

It turned out to be really a goalies' game. Porky Trotter at one end and Monkey-Grab at the other were both on top form.

At half-time it was a draw. At full-time, after a final ten minutes full of incident, Jawbone and Nut-Case Norris had each managed to slam full speed shots past the agile, hard-working 'keepers.

"Very satisfactory," said Bad-News Benson, as he blew the final whistle. "I'm proud of Lags Eleven and I think the Commander has a team worth its salt."

"Trust me, Mr. Benson," said Brilliant. "These Brimstone lads had it in 'em, but all they needed was a bit of interest and some hard coaching. Now I reckon I can go home with the boys. I never thought I'd say it, **but I miss dear old Grimwalls."**

MAN OVERBOARD

SOON Brilliant Genius and the Brimstone team were gathered in the boatshed.

"Haw, haw," Jawbone guffawed as he climbed on to the yacht. "Old Twirpy's had himself a soccer team for one day. He won't see **us** again."

"Okay, knock those chocks away," said Brilliant, climbing up the ladder to take the wheel. "Then jump aboard quick, for we'll go down this slipway like greased lighting."

With a muffled cheer the Brimstone lags crowded the deck as the boat began to move. It hit the loosened gate and went with a splash into the water beyond.

"All of you," barked Willie, tense at the wheel, "start haulin' the masts up. We'll have to set sail once we're in more open water."

Jawbone got his men working hard, and the yacht surged across the water towards a reed-edged channel. Then Brilliant turned urgently to Porky Trotter, who was standing miserably behind him.

"I don't wanna do this," bawled Porky. "I'd rather transfer to Grimwalls and play soccer."

"You don't have to do it, mate," said Willie. "Make

like you're falling overboard."

"Eh? Cripes, I **can't** swim," moaned Porky.

"All the better," grinned Willie, and gave him a push which sent him flying over the stern rail into the murky water.

Swiftly Brilliant started the auxiliary engine and the yacht forged on. But he himself ran to the stern and took a flying leap into the water.

"Man overboard!" he yelled. "Hey, Jawbone, take the wheel!"

Porky was thrashing about when Willie reached him in a few strokes and got a grip on him.

"Hey, you twits," Jawbone was yelling, "we can't wait for you. We're headin' for the sea!"

"Just what I'd hoped," spluttered Willie. "Hang on, Porky—I'm swimmin' back to the boatshed."

They reached the mud below the water-gate and turned to see the yacht, under half power, still surging away from them.

"There's no wind," Brilliant grinned, "so even if they hoisted the sails they wouldn't get anywhere. And that engine's gonna stop any second now. **There's only a pint of juice in the tank!"**

The engine sputtered into silence. The yacht had almost reached the channel, but something else seemed to be happening to it. It was sinking lower in the water, and as Willie helped Porky to scramble into the boatshed, he saw that it had ploughed into the mud and was stuck fast, water almost up to the gunwale, and the Brimstone prisoners dancing in fury on the deck.

At that moment Commander Twerpe-Trimble, Bad-News Benson, Lags Eleven and some warders came charging into the boatshed.

Willie was pretending to give Porky first-aid.

"My boat!" roared the Commander. "My soccer team!"

"Lucky I came for a stroll to get some air," said Brilliant Genius. "Saw this poor chap pushed into the water, so I dived in to save him. Don't know what happened to your boat, Governor. Reckon somebody must have left a couple of planks loose, or something."

Porky took his cue. "I tried to stop those silly fellows making a break for it," he groaned. "So they pushed me overboard, sir. I owe my life to this hero, **Brilliant Genius.**"

"Well," growled Bad-News, "those lags won't get anywhere now. Let 'em sweat till you can get some boats out, Commander."

"Good idea," said Twerpe-Trimble. "If they get over the side they'll sink waist-deep in mud."

"Mr. Benson, sir," said Willie, "isn't it time our coach left? We've got a long trip home to Grimwalls Prison."

"Right, lad," said Bad-News briskly. "Commander, we'll leave this to you. Done our part. Trained you a soccer team, but whether you can trust 'em to play away, I wouldn't like to say."

Brilliant nudged him. "Sir . . . Governor . . ." he wheedled. "Porky Trotter's worried. He thinks that lot'll bash him for trying to back out of the

Anchors away! Brilliant's at the helm, leading the great escape from Brimstone Jail.

prison break. He's a first-class 'keeper, a keen soccer player, and he's versatile. Fine type for a reserve 'keeper, or a full-back, in fact for the marvellous Lags Eleven, in fact."

"Humph!" Bad-News glanced suspiciously at him, but then approached the Commander. "I think this man Trotter might be in danger from those villains," he announced. "I'm ready to take him with me, Commander, and keep him under my care at Grimwalls Prison. Perhaps we can arrange a transfer between us, eh?"

"Good idea," said the Commander absently, staring at his yacht, sunk to the deck, with the baffled lags milling and stamping in their anger. "Leave it to you, Benson. I've got to ferry those men back and salvage my boat. Can't understand how she came to sink, though."

Only Brilliant Genius knew that, as he confided to Nut-Case Norris on the journey back to Grimwalls.

"Those geezers won't grass on me," he whispered, "even if they guess what really happened. Only you and me know, Nut-Case, that I pulled out the drain plugs in that boat. **I couldn't spoil my record by making a break from Grimwalls, could I? Haw-haw."**

THE END

BEAU BANNION STAR SPOTTER

BEAU BANNION WAS A FAMOUS FREELANCE SOCCER SCOUT. HIS SECRETARY, MISS ALICIA TIPPLES, WAS FINDING IT HARD TO GET USED TO HIS WHIRLWIND BEHAVIOUR AND UNUSUAL METHODS...

GOING SOMEWHERE, MR. BANNION?

SOUTH AMERICA, BABY... BY THE NEXT PLANE! I'LL BE IN TOUCH!

WHEN BANNION LANDED AT RIO PARADOR, A DEPUTATION OF ANXIOUS CLUB OFFICIALS GREETED HIM...

SENOR BANNION, WE ARE MOST GRATEFUL THAT YOU HAVE COME SO FAR IN ANSWER TO OUR APPEAL!

DON'T THANK ME, AMIGOS, UNTIL YOU'VE SEEN HOW MUCH IT'S GOING TO COST YOU! WHAT'S THE PROBLEM?

BEAU BANNION WAS DRIVEN AWAY FROM THE AIRPORT...

IT CONCERNS OUR WORLD-FAMOUS SUPER-STAR, PEDRO JUANEZ! AT LEAST - HE WAS OUR SUPER-STAR!

WE WILL TAKE YOU STRAIGHT TO THE RIO STADIUM! PEDRO IS PLAYING IN A MATCH WHICH HAS JUST BEGUN! YOU WILL SEE FOR YOURSELF!

AT THE STADIUM...

THERE IS YOUR PROBLEM, SENOR BANNION... PEDRO JUANEZ - NUMBER NINE!

WHERE'S THE PROBLEM? TO ME HE LOOKS A GREAT PERFORMER!

WAIT, SENOR BANNION, AND YOU WILL SOON CHANGE YOUR MIND!

JUANEZ FAILED TO PICK UP A RETURN PASS...

SEE! HE HAS MISSED IT!

YOU WANT MIRACLES, AMIGO? HE HAD NO HOPE! THERE WAS TOO MUCH PACE ON THE BALL!

BUT THEN...

IMBECILE! DOLT! USELESS CARRION!

BUT HE NEEDN'T HAVE BLOWN HIS STACK! IT WAS AN EASILY-MADE MISTAKE!

MUST I DO EVERYTHING MYSELF?

JUANEZ REGAINED POSSESSION BRILLIANTLY AND BEAT THE DEFENCE WITH A MAGICAL BODY-SWERVE...

I JUST DON'T SEE WHAT YOU CATS ARE ACTING SO SCALDED ABOUT! HE'S GREAT!

BUT THEN BEAU HAD TO THINK AGAIN..

POWEE! HOW DID HE MISS? WHAT HAPPENED?

HE LOSES HIS TEMPER, SENOR! THERE WILL BE WORSE!

AND A FEW MINUTES LATER...

AAAARGH! YOU PEASANT!

JUANEZ RUSHED AT THE REFEREE, SCREAMING AN APPEAL FOR A FREE-KICK...

JUANEZ IS CRAZY IF HE THINKS HE CAN CLAIM A FOUL!

IT WAS A PERFECTLY FAIR CHARGE!

THE SOUTH AMERICAN LET HIS TEMPER GET THE BETTER OF HIM...

MAN, HE'S CRAZY! EVEN THE GREAT PEDRO JUANEZ CAN'T GET AWAY WITH CLOBBERING THE REFEREE!

YOU SEE OUR PROBLEM? PEDRO USED TO BE THE NICEST PLAYER, ON AND OFF THE FIELD! NOW HE IS IMPOSSIBLE! WE MUST REPLACE HIM BEFORE HE RUINS THE CLUB!

I GET THE PICTURE, AMIGO!

FINDING THE RIGHT PLAYER WON'T BE EASY! FOOTBALLERS LIKE PEDRO JUANEZ DON'T GROW ON TREES! BUT IF HE EXISTS, THE BEAU BANNION SYSTEM WILL FIND HIM! I'M SENDING ALL THIS DATA OFF TO MY SECRETARY IN ENGLAND!

MISS TIPPLES RECEIVED HER INSTRUCTIONS AND WENT TO WORK...

THIS IS THE TOUGHEST ASSIGNMENT EVEN MR. BANNION HAS EVER HANDLED! IT COULD BE HIS FIRST FAILURE!

WHEN THE SYSTEM DELIVERED ITS ANSWER, MISS TIPPLES BECAME INCREASINGLY SURE THAT BANNION HAD MET HIS MATCH...

THAT CAN'T BE RIGHT! EITHER MR. BANNION HAS SLIPPED UP, OR I'VE MADE A MISTAKE—AND I DON'T THINK THAT'S POSSIBLE! BUT I'LL GO THROUGH IT AGAIN, JUST TO MAKE SURE!

THE SAME ANSWER CAME OUT A SECOND TIME...

AH, WELL, IT WASN'T MY MISTAKE! I'M HERE TO DO AS I'M TOLD! BUT THEY'LL SKIN MR. BANNION ALIVE WHEN THIS GETS TO RIO PARADOR!

BUT BEAU SHOWED NO SIGNS OF EMBARRASSMENT WHEN HE REPORTED TO THE CLUB OFFICIALS...

HOT FROM MY LONDON OFFICE, AMIGOS! THE FILE ON THE MAN YOUR CLUB NEEDS!

BUT WHEN THE OFFICIALS SAW THE FILE...

IS THIS SOME KIND OF JOKE?

HOW DARE YOU INSULT US?

ACCORDING TO THIS, THE PLAYER WE NEED TO REPLACE PEDRO JUANEZ, IS —

—PEDRO JUANEZ!

BANNION'S KEEN EARS DETECTED THE FAINT SOUND OF STEALTHY MOVEMENT AND HE REACTED LIKE LIGHTNING...

BUT BEAU-BOY IS WIDE AWAKE!

YOU'RE IN NO STATE TO GET MIXED UP IN ANY TROUBLE! BUT YOU CAN MAKE YOURSELF USEFUL! CALL THE COPS WHILE I GO DOWN FOR A LOOK-SEE!

THE STRANGE SOUND LED BANNION TO THE CELLARS...

YOU WERE RIGHT AGAIN, BEAU-BABY— IT ISN'T MICE!

HE'S SEEN US!

DON'T LET HIM GET AWAY!

SHOOT HIM DOWN!

THE POLICE BROKE INTO THE HOUSE IN THE NICK OF TIME...

POLICE! WE'RE TRAPPED!

YOU SAID IT, MAN!